Other books by Eduard Petiška
telling of the past of the Czech Lands,
published in English

A Treasury of Tales from the Kingdom of Bohemia

The Lives of St. Wenceslas, St. Ludmila and St. Adalbert

Charles IV.
The King from the Golden Cradle

Beautiful Stories of Golden Prague

The Golem

In preparation:

On the Famous Deeds of Castle Lords
and on Coats of Arms

The illustrations are from the book "Diadochus" (1602)
by Bartoloměj Paprocký z Hlohol
and from old Czech prints
from the XIXth century.

The publisher thanks all those who contributed
with advice and help, or by loans,
towards collecting the rare illustrations.

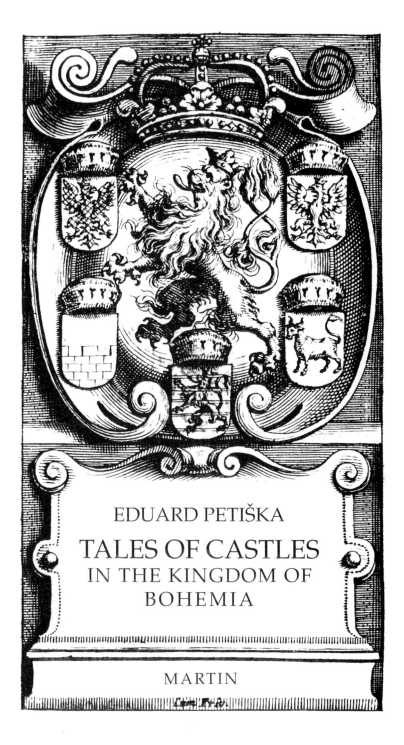

EDUARD PETIŠKA

TALES OF CASTLES
IN THE KINGDOM OF
BOHEMIA

MARTIN

Judgment And Choice, The Castle over the Vltava, The Great Leap, Battle And Betrayal, Magician of the New Age, The Petrovský Band, Two Nights in Cheb, The Sacrifice, On Ladies of the Castle, Záviš of Falkenštejn, From the Stories of Imperial Castles, A Mysterious Castle, A Magical Goblet, The Knights Templars in Bohemia, An Invincible Castle, Vojmil And Svatava, The Knights of Blaník

by Eduard Petiška

The Karlštejn Devils, Nightingales at Křivoklát, The Phantoms of Kokořín, The Archduke and Dragons, The Birth of War, The Secret of Šternberk Castle, How the Name Kutná Hora Originated, An Old Prophesy, On Love and Betrayal, The Gnomes of Kutná Hora, Mělník Wine, The Mělník Treasure, The Mysterious Gift, The Knights of Mělník, The First Guest, The Secret of Točník Castle, The Strange Stone from Loket Castle, The Knight of Náchod, The Daughter of Forefather Čech, The Eagle's Nest, The Valdštejn Dragons, Two Voices, A Late Decision

by Jan M. Vaniš

ISBN 80–901744–2–6

PREFACE

You are opening a book of legends of the castles of the Bohemian kingdom.

You are opening a book of stories of ancient times, stories that have been told by the light of torches and candles from generation to generation, for centuries these stories have accompanied the Czech nation.

This book is a selection from the wealth of stories about Czech castles, castles that rank worthily among the most famous and most beautiful castles of old Europe.

This selection of ancient tales on Czech castles is intended for those who would like to know more about the romantic places they have visited. It is here for those who want to know not only the tangible monuments of the past, but to learn more of the mood of these fairytale castles, to enter into bygone times, lend an ear to ancient events...

Anyone who wants to know the ancient history of the kingdom of Bohemia more closely and completely can read the book "A Treasury of Tales from the Kingdom of Bohemia" published by the Martin Publishers, that will lead them through the old stories from the coming of the tribe of Czechs to their new country.

Welcome to the path through the destiny of the people of one of the ancient European kingdoms, you are invited to places where once not only the future of the Czech Lands was shaped, but that of many nations.

The gates of the old Bohemian castles invite you.

Today they are open for the hundreds of thousands of visitors from all over the world that pass through them every year.

The gateway of legends is open too. Beyond that gateway live people who are long since dead, kings, knights, ordinary folk...

People who have their hopes, their dreams and troubles so like ours, and who are mirrored only in the imprint they have left on old stories.

7

One day our time too will only be reflected in stories...
Stories that perhaps are coming into being just today...

Let us enter the ancient castle gates.

Let us enter the gateway of legends.

Ruined buildings rise from the rubble, banners wave again on the long deserted towers, plumes on the helmets of knights and kings flutter in the wind...

People long dead live again, they address you. Forgotten stories are repeated...

The Bohemian castles and their vanished inmates await you...

Eduard Martin

LIBUŠÍN

JUDGMENT AND CHOICE

In ancient days more than fifteen Slav tribes were settled in Bohemia. Some of them were strong and powerful, others weak, the names of some of them have been kept till our times and the names of others have been lost. They have been blown away by trickling, tireless time.

The tribe of the Czechs lived in the very heart of the country and their judge was Libuše, daughter of Krok. One day a group of men burst into the courtyard of Libuše's castle. Two of them were quarrelling loudly and the others in the group were agreeing first with one, then with the other and, as usually happens, they were amused at the anger of those two. Suddenly one of the men contending for justice grabbed his opponent by the beard and dragged him forward. The bearded man entwined his fingers in his rival's hair. They yelled and cursed each other and the group of on-lookers encouraged them. The noise filled the courtyard and Libuše came out of her log castle.

When the two ruffians saw Krok's noble daughter they ceased struggling and bowed down, as though they knew nothing better than loving kindness. But as soon as Libuše asked why they had been making such a din, they started yelling at each other, each accusing the other of wrong-doing and trying to shout each other down. They hoped that right would be on the side of him who shouted loudest. The case in point was confused, but simple. The bearded man thought that the clean-shaven one had not observed the borders between their plots of land and had used another's as if it were his own. And not only that, but he had insultingly snapped his fingers under the bearded man's nose and the bearded man had no intention of standing for that.

Libuše justly listened to both complaining sides and to the witnesses and wisely judged on which side the right lay. Although the bearded man was not harmed by the judgment, he felt he had been wronged. He had wanted to crush his opponent and wished him the cruellest of punishments. When it did not happen like that he was seized with rage and he began to shake his head derisively and strike his stick on the ground. His chin was quivering with agitation and he shouted:

"Shame, shame! But what could I expect of a woman judge? What do women know of men's disputes? Not even the highest rank or the biggest castle adds to their sense. We all know it," he turned to the men standing in the courtyard, "we all know that women have long hair but they are short on good sense."

Such injustice pained Libuše. But she did not let her feelings be seen and said:

"You confuse justice with cruelty. You do not like the rule of a woman, because she is gentle and allows you freedom. You think there is good sense only where there is punishment with a rod of iron. Very well, you shall have what you wish. Tomorrow let the people assemble in this courtyard. If all of them wish for a man's rule, I shall announce to you whom I shall take as my husband. He will be your prince."

That very day Libuše summoned her sisters from Kazín and Tetín and consulted with them the whole night, and all three made sacrifices to the gods and tried to see into the future, for all of them had the precious gift of prophesy.

And hardly had daylight thrown its first timid shadow than people from near and far gathered at Libuše's castle and filled the courtyard and the area round the castle. And the higher the sun rose, the more numerous was the crowd, and they poured over the road and the gateway like stormy waves. Libuše came out of her timbered palace and addressed the crowd:

"Have you decided to exchange my rule for that of a man?"

"Yes, yes," came a roar from all sides.

"Do not forget that it is easy to seat a prince upon the

throne, but difficult to unseat him once he is there. As it is your wish, and you want to throw yourselves on the mercy of a man, I will tell you the place where your future prince lives, and I will tell you his name."

"We want a prince, a prince," the crowd cried.

Libuše raised her hand to the mountains, lying blue in the autumn mists, and called:

"There, beyond those mountains runs the river Bílina. On its banks you will find a village that is named Stadice. Not far from this village there is fallow land and a man is ploughing it with two striped oxen. One of these animals has a white head and a white stripe in front, the other has a white forehead, back and hind legs. The man ploughing with them is Přemysl, the prince who will rule you. And his offspring too will rule you. Take with you a robe such as befits the princely rank, find Přemysl and bring back a ruler for you and a husband for me."

But the messengers who were to look for Přemysl hesitated, because they did not know the way. Libuše noticed their indecision and advised them:

"Bring my horse out before the castle. Where he goes so you too should go. He knows the way and he knows the place."

They brought Libuše's white horse in front of the castle gateway, and the horse made for the forest through which a path had been cut. So they took that path behind him. And the forest then hid within itself a salt spring that was still waiting to be discovered, and a legend as yet unborn waited for the town that would be called Slaný (salty). Then Libuše's white horse came out on a plain and the messengers saw in the distance the hill named Říp, from which Forefather Čech first viewed this country. And the distant hill of their ancestors accompanied them and turned after them like a giant head half hidden beyond the horizon. In the blue and gold web of the autumn sunshine the hill had a kindly look, and it seemed to the messengers that it loomed up as a sign of luck and good hope.

The horse then trod heedfully along the river Ohře,

11

till it found a ford. It entered the river and drank, for the day was dry and warm. When it had slaked its thirst, it crossed the shallow water to the other bank and took an almost indiscernible path to a broad meadow. There it hastened its step, and the nearer they came to the Central Mountains, the more quickly it trotted. He scents his destination, the messengers were pleased. But they still had to cross the mountains and only there, when their horses hoofs again trod soft grass, they saw a village. There the horse neighed.

"Hey," they called to a boy who was crossing the field, "is this Stadice?"

"Yes, it is," the boy nodded.

"And does a man live here whom they call Přemysl?"

"He's ploughing over there," the boy pointed.

They went in that direction and found a well-built man ploughing a fallow field with oxen, and one had a white head and a white stripe in front, and the other had a white forehead and its back and hind legs were white.

Libuše's white horse stopped in the first furrow of freshly turned soil and stood as if nailed to the ground, waiting for a word of command.

"All hail to you, Přemysl," called the messengers, "all hail to our chosen prince."

Přemysl pulled up his oxen and listened to the messengers in silence.

"Unharness your oxen," the messengers told him, "put on this princely robe, and mount Libuše's white horse. We are envoys from the tribe of the Czechs, and all our people have sent us to bring them a prince, and our mistress Libuše has sent us to bring her a husband."

As soon as the words were out of their mouths Přemysl, as if he had been expecting this news, took the oxen from the plough and told them:

"Run off to where you came from."

The beasts ran off and disappeared as if by magic. And afterwards it used to be said amongst the people that the two animals rose into the air as if they had wings and a nearby cliff swallowed them up as water does a pebble.

Přemysl struck the hazel wand with which he had been driving his oxen into the earth, and the wand grew green and three branches sprouted from it with leaves and nuts. The messengers were amazed at this wonder. Then Přemysl reached into his bast bag and got out bread and a piece of cheese and invited the messengers to eat with him. And the fresh grass was the floor of that banqueting hall, its arch the sky with larks, the table was a bast bag and the tablecloth an unbleached kerchief.

While they ate and drank pure water from a jug, two branches of the miraculous hazel faded, withered and fell. But the third branch grew more and more strongly. Then the messengers dared to ask what this wonder might mean. Přemysl replied:

"That growing hazel branch is a picture of my tribe. Though it gives birth to many masters, only one will reign. It is only a pity, a great pity, that you found me so soon. If you had come when I had finished ploughing the last furrow on this fallow land, there would never have been want in Bohemia. There would have been enough bread for everyone for all time, no one in the country would have known hunger."

Přemysl donned the princely robe, put on boots that befitted a prince and picked up his old bast sandals and took them with him.

"Why, master," they asked him, "are you taking your old, worn sandals? Are not the boots on your feet better?"

"I am taking them with me," smiled Přemysl, "so that my descendants shall not forget from where they came. So that they shall not unjustly oppress those who walk the world in bast shoes. So that they shall not forget that by nature we are all equal."

The messengers, with the new prince in their midst, crossed the mountains joyfully and hurried to the familiar ford and back to Libuše's castle. Libuše's white horse bore Přemysl lightly, as though he were dancing. Along the way people recognized the white horse, and as it was already generally known whom he was carrying, they greeted Přemysl and joined in the procession.

Libuše saw the crowd of people from the castle. She came out with her maidens and servants to meet the new prince and her husband.

In the castle they were preparing the wedding feast. The spits were turning over the fire, and the rich scent of roasting meat was a pleasant invitation to the guests. No one could remember such a wedding feast.

In the evening, when night first touched the feasters with its cool fingers, they moved in closer to the fires and the compact circle strengthened their fellow-feeling and the mead loosened their tongues. Songs soared into the darkness and the glow over Libuše's castle spread the good news far and wide around the country. They were celebrating a prince, a wedding and friendship between the Lemuz tribe, to which Přemysl belonged, and the tribe of the Czechs, from which Libuše came.

And in those ancient times there were more than fifteen Slav tribes in Bohemia. But in the end it was the Czechs, who settled in the very heart of the country, who gave their name to the whole land and all its people.

Vyšehrad

VYŠEHRAD

THE CASTLE OVER THE VLTAVA

Once, long, long ago, a castle stood over the Vltava with wooden ramparts and a timbered palace within the ramparts. Later it was given the name Vyšehrad (High Castle). It stood on the right bank of the river on a tall cliff, the foot of which was lapped by restless waves. The castle stood as firm as the will of the princes who ruled in it.

It is said that here Prince Přemysl would sit on a stone princely throne and, with Princess Libuše, would receive reports from all over his country, here he gave judgments and advice.

Under his rule the country changed ever more quickly. Thick forests retreated before fields, and between the fields hard-working hands built settlements and forts and castles. Prince Přemysl advised his people well. The more forts and castles there were in the land the better the settlers could defend themselves against enemy invasion. In times of war they retreated behind the bulwarks and fortifications, built up supplies there and herded in their cattle. Behind the fortifications they preserved their lives and that of their families.

The tribe of the Czechs increased, and there was a need to find more and more places to settle. Princess Libuše, asked where the most suitable place would be for a new settlement, answered: "Settle in a place where you will find the four elements in mutual harmony. Fertile, life-giving earth, pure water, healthy air and enough fuel for fire, where the trees afford both wood and shade. If harmony reigns amongst the elements, you will want for nothing."

Many families then settled in the land according to Libuše's advice, and their fields yielded a rich harvest and their herds multiplied. A cheerful smoke rose to the heavens from the fireplaces of the new homes.

16

It is said that at that time the prince's servant Okrs approached him and asked for a place where he could build a castle for himself. Přemysl was fond of Okrs and he allowed him to build a castle west of the Vltava, on a site protected by the steepness of the banks and the water. It is said that the castle was named after its founder, Okrs. But in time the mouths of the people changed the name to Okoř.

But it was not a lucky star that shone on the building of Okoř castle. Of the family that settled there came Šárka, and from her came misery, hatred and treachery. In those days many settlements and forts grew up. It was like a starry night when a multitude of stars shine, but the moon, that surpasses all the stars in brightness and magnitude, that rules over them, has not yet come up.

Once when Prince Přemysl visited Libušín castle with Princess Libuše, they mounted together with their company to the highest point of the castle. It was evening, and in the glow of the setting sun the landscape spread out on all sides, showing traces of the work of human hands. Fields alternated with settlements and pastures, the forest had retreated to the horizon and there held guard in close formation. The dazzling sun was descending into the forest and the shadow of the castle fell to the east. Princess Libuše turned to the hazy blue shadows of advancing night and suddenly everything on the earth and in the atmosphere was seized by a great silence. No one of the company spoke, the wind held its breath and the birds, that had been warbling till that moment, fell silent in the tree-tops. The princess stretched out her hand to the east, and as if she were touching something far away in the clouds and evening mists, she moved her fingers gently and spoke:

"I see a great castle and its glory reaches to the stars. The place lies hidden in deep woods, from the north it is protected by the valley of the Brusnice stream, from the south by a wide rocky hill. The river Vltava pushes its way beneath its slopes. Go there and in the midst of a wood you will see a man hewing out threshold. There build

17

a castle and name it, according to the hewn threshold, Praha.* And as even great men bow their heads on a threshold, so will they bow them before this castle."

Prince Přemysl and his company looked in that direction, but all they saw was the advancing night. The future was hidden in it like a precious stone in a hill.

For a further moment the Princess's white hand pointed into the distance, then the prophetic spirit left her and the sparkle of her eyes was extinguished. And, as happens with prophets and poets, when Libuše's enthusiasm faded, it was awakened in those who listened to her, and they started at once to prepare for their journey.

At the break of a new day messengers set off towards the east, to find the place the Princess had spoken of. They came to the valley of the stream and to the rocky hill and entered the wood, from which regular blows could be heard. They found a man hewing out the threshold of a house.

They did not hesitate and went to work. They felled trees,built log-huts, raised earthworks. Thus on the left bank of the Vltava Prague castle grew up, wooden like Vyšehrad, but more spacious and more splendid. The name Praha spread from mouth to mouth throughout the length of the land, and foreign merchants carried it to distant countries.

Princess Libuše saw into the future, and she also saw into the interior of the earth. Her prophesies are said to have determined which hill had gold within it and which silver. Indeed legend tells that it was then that gold was discovered in Jílové and silver in Kutná Hora. And we hear that in those good old days there was such an abundance of silver and even of gold, that in places it sprouted from the earth like a sapling and it was enough just to break it off. It was then that a man was digging for gold near Jílové and found such a nugget that it weighed more than the prince and princess together. He sent this astounding and massive chunk of gold to Prince

*Práh = threshold in Czech. Translator's note.

18

Přemysl at Vyšehrad. Přemysl consulted Princess Libuše and they summoned a sculptor who made a golden statue in the likeness of a man sitting on a princely throne. They had a special hut built for the golden idol, and they went to bow down to it there and brought it sacrifices in gratitude for the gifts afforded to the Czechs by their fertile and metal-rich land. They called the golden idol Zelú.

Gold and silver was stored in the underground halls of Vyšehrad, which are said to have been the treasure-house of the tribe since the days of Krok. And the son of Přemysl and Libuše, Nezamysl, had a golden cradle.

The years passed by, and because they were happy years for the country and for the royal family, they passed quickly. The royal son Nezamysl was already trying to stretch his bow-string and to lift his father's sword. Libuše's heart felt father's pride in her son, but also sorrow at the passage of time, that rules even rulers. She told her maidens to take the golden cradle and to follow her. The Princess stopped at the place below Vyšehrad where the river had hollowed out such a depth that the surface was darkened.

"Let the cradle down into the depths," she told the maidens.

The heavy gold cradle sunk into the water, there was a brief flash and it disappeared. But the princess followed it with fixed gaze and saw its long fall through the water and through the centuries that it must travel. And she saw light in the depths of the ages, and at one time it was the glow of the sun and at another fire, and she heard noise and shouting, and at one time it was cheering and song, and at another weeping and lament. The golden cradle sank deeper and deeper amongst the waters of tears.

"Hide yourself, hide!" called the princess, "and one day, purified by the tears of those who live in this land, you will emerge from the waves and good hands will grasp you and lay within you a child who will bring salvation to his people and his country."

The princess returned to Vyšehrad in silence.

And the cradle was like a golden grain, sown to bear fruit one day. So too the secret Vyšehrad treasure was like a precious grain that would provide bread for all the hungry when the land suffered the greatest need. But the most precious grain sown in the future was the youngest generation, to which Nezamysl belonged.

Libuše longed to see into his future too. She offered up a burnt sacrifice to the idol Zelú and prepared herself to gaze into times that lay far ahead of her. As she searched her son's path, she heard within her a soft, insistent voice. It was the voice of death.

Sadly the princess left the golden idol, found Prince Přemysl and said to him:

"I have heard the voice, it called me and called on me to bid farewell and set out on the road on which my father Krok departed and my mother Niva and my sister Kazi. Summon our son Nezamysl and the elders and our faithful company. It is time to bid farewell."

And as one who, leaving his father's house, looks back when already on the way, before the beloved place is hidden from sight, the princess looked around her. Her sight was weakening, she could hardly distinguish the trees and cliffs on the opposite bank, and the Vltava below Vyšehrad seemed to her to flow into a wavering stream of pale mist. Somewhere over there was Strahov forest, and that way her castle Praha, whose glory was beginning to shine.

The princess allowed herself to be led to her bed. Nearby things were blurred before her eyes and passed her by, for they stood in life and the princess was leaving life. But far-off things she saw clearly and precisely, and on the lips of mute fate she read words that were as yet unformed.

And when those she loved gathered around her bed Princess Libuše's wisdom spoke for the last time.

In a voice growing ever more distant she spoke of unity and loyalty, without which there is no strength, of love and bravery, without which life is but a brief interval between birth and death, of eternity, that we bear on our shoulders so that we may give it to future generations.

Then she turned to her husband Přemysl. She warned him of the dangers lurking in the future and told him of the hope that, like a lucky star, leads on all those who do not lose courage.

Finally she turned to Nezamysl, her little son. Nezamysl was the continuation of the House of Přemyslides, he was that precious grain sown in the incalculable times ahead. She stroked his hair, and everyone who saw that movement of her outstretched arm was reminded of her prophesy and understood that she was bequeathing the glory of this land and its people to the youngest of them.

Princess Libuše died and all the settlements and castles of the Czechs were filled with weeping and lamentation, as children bewail the death of a loving mother. But Libuše's prophesies sustained the courage of her people for centuries. They gave it strength in cruel times and fanned the spark of pride and self-confidence into a flaming fire.

During the reign of Prince Křesomysl there stood between Beroun and Příbram, below the rolling slopes of Housiny, the fortress of Neumětely. It stood in meadows, protected by bulwarks and ramparts, that enclosed it as a ring encloses a finger. In front of the ramparts was a deep moat, and the water that was let into the moat prevented intruders from approaching the ramparts. The thane Horymír lived in this fortress and presided over the surrounding land. So legend relates.

During the years of Křesomysl's rule a longing for gold and silver spread immensely amongst the people. Many of them left their villages and made their way to the gold-bearing rivers in the south of our country. Many a ploughman exchanged his plough for a pan in which he washed river sand, instead of sowing grain for bread he picked grains of gold from the sand. Others went to places indicated by ancient prophesy and opened up the earth and broke the rocks, to take precious metal from the heart of the land. Life shifted from the fields and hamlets to the banks of rivers and to hills and mountains. The forest sent wild weeds and brushwood into the orphaned fields and the deserted hamlets. It reclaimed soil that man had previously taken from it.

And there were many who feared for the state of the land. They came to Prince Křesomysl in Vyšehrad and called for the situation to be righted. Horymír of Neumětely was one of those who came before the prince.

"Just look, Prince," he complained, "our fields are ploughed by wild boar, our fields are sown with the seeds of the forest and rocky hillsides, our fields are harvested by the wind. Where are we to get bread, if everyone goes away to search for metal? We shall waste away with hunger and starvation will also afflict those who have set out for the rivers and the mountains. Give orders, Prince, that the people should keep to the old customs and return to their fields and their flocks."

Prince Křesomysl assented to Horymír's words and promised that he would put things to rights. But scarcely had Horymír left for the Neumětely fortress, than the prince's mind inclined in the other direction. Křesomysl found it pleasant to accept precious metals from the gold-diggers and to swell the princely treasure with both taxes and gifts. Greed for the wealth that was hidden in the earth had seized him too.

If I take the side of Horymír, the side of the dissatisfied thanes, I shall gain nothing for myself, the prince reflected, but if I take the side of the gold-diggers my Vyšehrad treasure will increase.

And because he had enough bread himself, the hunger of others did not weigh upon him.

The thanes waited in vain for the promised righting of affairs, Horymír waited in vain for the prince's favour. It seemed that the old customs were irretrievably lost.

But the news of Horymír's complaint spread amongst the gold-diggers. It was passed from quarry to quarry, from pit to pit, and hatred of Horymír flared up sharply, for not one of the gold-diggers wanted to leave his new craft.

"The best thing would be to kill Horymír," advised the hottest heads.

"We'll stuff bread down his gullet till it suffocates him," cried others.

And the ones joined with the others and they set out for Horymír's fortress. Their motive was revenge.

Horymír saw from afar the rampageous people approaching, armed with hoes, crowbars and clubs. He could not stand up to such a multitude. So he went to find his best friend. His best friend was not a man, but the faithful horse Šemík. Šemík turned his big, wise eyes on Horymír and he read in his face that disaster was upon them. Horymír stroked the horse, swung onto his back and called:

"Rise up, Šemík!"

Šemík reared up and leapt with Horymír across the ramparts and the moat and disappeared into the forest.

Then the gold-diggers overran Horymír's estate like locusts, destroying and plundering, they scattered the stacks, took the corn and in the end they resorted to fire. That completed the destruction of Horymír's estates.

Then the gold-diggers wound their way from Neumětely to their work, in high spirits at their easy victory, and on the way they jeered:

"Horymír need not fear hunger any more. Now he will just be hungry."

But violence never comes singly. It calls for further violence. When Horymír came home in the evening and found nothing but ashes and smouldering beams, he swore by the first star over the horizon and by all the mysterious beings of the waters, the meadows and the forests that the gold-diggers should pay for that injustice.

He leapt up on Šemík and rushed through the forest and the darkness to the gold-diggers' mines. On the way he called the spirits of the night to his aid, and the spirits flew down to him and rushed forward with him.

Wherever the seekers after metal had opened the earth, Horymír closed it again. The night spirits helped him to sweep stones, clay and sand into the holes and pits. They helped him to set fire to the gold-diggers' huts and cabins and raced hotfoot on their way.

But in the morning Horymír stood among the prince's courtiers in Vyšehrad as fresh as if he had slept all night.

Soon a long procession of gold-diggers came to Vyšehrad, they shook their fists in the direction of Horymír.

"Is it true what these men say?" Křesomysl asked Horymír. "And if it is true, why do you harm them? He who harms them harms me."

"Is it not beyond the power of a single man to do so much work in a single night?" Horymír replied. He did not say whether what the gold-diggers spoke was the truth, nor did he say it was lies.

But the gold-diggers knew of no other culprit. It was Horymír whom they had most harmed, and so they were convinced that he too had harmed them most.

When the prince realised how long it would take before the gold-diggers could undo the damage and before the earth would again yield up its treasure, when he realised the greatness of his loss, he fell into a great fury. He commanded that Horymír, ravager of the prince's treasury, should be imprisoned and guarded until such time as sentence should be passed on him.

Křesomysl called a council of elders, but his anger shortened the consultation. The sentence was: Horymír shall pay for his deeds with his own head. And because many of the gold-diggers asserted that they had recognized Horymír as he galloped towards them in the light of the flames with drawn sword, the prince declared that Horymír should die by his own sword.

The gold-diggers in the Vyšehrad courtyard burst into cheers. Horymír bowed his head, but at once raised it again.

"Prince," he said, "if I must indeed depart this life, grant me one wish, that I may for the last time take a ride on my horse."

Křesomysl nodded that the condemned man's last wish should be fulfilled. But he ordered that the castle gates should be shut. Servants brought Šemík to Horymír, Horymír whispered something to him and leapt up onto him. As soon as he was in the saddle he shouted and the horse spun round beneath him. He shouted a second time and Šemík took off and made a great leap from the gates to the ramparts. Křesomysl and the whole gathering were amazed. Horymír shouted for the third time and called:

"Rise up, Šemík!"

Those who stood nearby said that they heard Šemík answer in a human voice:

"Hold on, Master."

And like an arrow leaving the string of a bow, the horse and rider rose into the air, passing over the ramparts and the hollows below the cliff, over the shining surface of the Vltava, landing on the opposite bank of the river. It is said that the tracks of his hoofs were long to be seen in the stone.

In Vyšehrad everyone ran to the ramparts and they saw that both horse and rider were alive and sound and that they were making for home, for Neumětely. The prince was dumbfounded as were the elders and the people.

Prince Křesomysl was brought to relent by the persuasion of the councillors and by his own fear. For who could survive such a leap but one who is protected by the gods? He sent messengers to the Neumětely fortress to announce to Horymír that he was forgiven.

Horymír outlived the gold-diggers' hatred, the prince's anger and the great leap, but his horse had injured himself by that leap. From that day he began to waste away.

"My dear Master," Šemík addressed Horymír one day, "my strength is rapidly failing, and soon we shall have to part. I fulfilled your wish, now you can fulfil mine. Do not let the crows and ravens nor the wolves scatter me about the land, but bury me before the gates of your court. So shall I be with you even after death."

Horymír fulfilled his Šemík's wish and for centuries the whole country has told of their faithful friendship.

DĚVÍN

BATTLE AND BETRAYAL

Old legends tell of the ancient rights of women. Women chose their husbands and the husbands lived in their wives' families.

When Princess Libuše, who defended the rights of women, died, the women lost their advocate. Prince Přemysl was on the side of the men. Theirs was the power and the right to rule. And just as once a man had mocked women before Libuše's court, saying they had long hair but were short on brains, so now a woman rose amongst the people and ridiculed the bearded mens' chins dripping with mead. The name of that young woman was Vlasta. She had been in Princess Libuše's escort and she bore hard the changes that spread from Vyšehrad and the forts to the villages and lonely farmsteads.

Vlasta gathered girls and young women around her. They all liked her words and none of those who followed her wanted to submit to the mastery of men.

On the left bank of the Vltava, opposite Vyšehrad, rose a long-topped hill. Vlasta took her maidens there and called on them to build a castle. The girls agreed enthusiastically and they did build a strong castle. They lived there as men live in castles, they practised shooting with the bow and rode out hunting in the Vltava forests. Prince Přemysl looked out perturbed from the heights of Vyšehrad at the new maidens' castle on the opposite bank of the river. He had a council called of the leading men of the tribe and he said to them:

"You certainly know of the new castle that the girls have built and that they call Děvín. This night I had an evil dream. Because of this bad dream and the unhappy castle I have summoned you. Listen to what I dreamed. I thought I saw a young maid who charged through our land as if crazed, with flying hair and contorted face. The streams ran with blood instead of water and the maid, like a rabid wolf, drank of this blood. Then she ran up to me and offered me too a bowl of blood."

The men listened to Přemysl's speech and they smiled. Děvín, they thought to themselves, is but a girl's game, and after a time every game tires. What sort of warriors could women ever be? And they ignored Přemysl's warning and listened only to their own conceit.

In the meantime Vlasta prepared the girls in Děvín for battle with the men. She divided the garrison of girls into three parts. She chose from the wisest and most courageous counsellors and guards, who stood guard over the castle. She taught the most beautiful girls flattering speeches and beguiling ways with men. They then lured men with sweet words and pleasant looks, just as huntsmen lure game with decoys. Woe to the man who fell into the clutches of such a beauty. He was annihilated. The third group of girls trained in using arms.

One of the worst things was that not a single man lived in Děvín, though in Vyšehrad and other castles and in the villages plenty of women still lived who were Vlasta's spies and who procured both weapons and horses for Děvín. So it happened that the men had neither enough weapons nor enough horses, and Vlasta and her counsellors knew their every movement, but the men had no news of the strength of the girls.

"It will be enough for us to advance on Děvín," said the men, "it will be enough for them just to see from Děvín a column of warriors, and they will take fright and open the gates to us."

In vain did Prince Přemysl warn them, he counselled them in vain.

The men assembled, each of them grabbed some weapon, but none of them believed that he would use a weapon. They advanced towards the maidens' castle without Přemysl and in cheerful mood. They were relying on feminine fear. The men climbed the hill towards the maidens' castle, and it seemed as if life had died out in Děvín. There was not a movement anywhere.

"You see?" the men called to one another, "no sooner do we show ourselves, and they hide from us like mice."

They went forward, not knowing they were watched from the castle by as many eyes as there were arrow slits in the ramparts. When they approached within shooting distance, the gates of Děvín flew open and girls on horseback with spears rushed out amongst the amazed men, headed by Vlasta, their commander. She herself pierced with her spear seven of the best men who, stunned with astonishment, never even raised their swords. The archeresses, whom the men had laughed at till then, sent a cloud of arrows over the confused warriors. The men's ranks wavered, some fell, others limped to the nearby forest, some still tried to encourage one another, but in vain. Vlasta and her maiden warriors held the field.

Sadly did the men return to Vyšehrad. Too late they recognized that Přemysl had spoken wisely. Tidings of the men's defeat spread round the country. All women held up their heads proudly. The thought of Děvín gave them strength. Some were indeed proud, but for love of their men did not leave them. Some were blinded by pride and they fled to Děvín. But to some pride gave new eyes, and the husbands of those women went out into the woods at night. They were afraid to sleep at their wives' sides, lest their lives should be taken from them in sleep.

The maidens' army grew from day to day. Armed gangs of girls rode through the land, and wherever they heard that a woman was still living in harmony with her husband, they shattered their content with cunning or with arms.

Slowly and with difficulty the men began to arm and to get horses. This time Prince Přemysl would not allow the fight to begin till the men were properly armed. Until then they were to be cautious and not believe even the most flattering girlish words. Yet always someone was to be found who did believe honeyed words from maidens' mouths and doubted the prince's good advice.

At that time Prince Přemysl sent one of his men, Ctirad, to settle a dispute between two clans, who had settled in a distant place on the left river bank. The whole of Vyšehrad knew of Ctirad's journey, and what Vyšehrad knew soon came to be known in Děvín. And at once there were girls who were ready to prepare a trap for Ctirad. They chose the most beautiful amongst them, Šárka, and went with her to the forest till they reached the path that Ctirad must take with his company. Here by the wayside they sat the lovely Šárka on an up-rooted tree trunk and bound her so firmly with straps that they bit into her skin. And so bitter was Šárka's hatred of men that she felt no pain, only delight at the trap being sprung. When the girls had bound Šárka, they laid a jug of mead beside her, hung a hunting horn on her neck and left her there. They hid in the forest not far away, together with their horses, and waited for their moment.

Šárka started weeping and wailing till the tree-covered valley echoed with her cries and multiplied them till the frightened birds deserted their nests.

Ctirad and his men heard her lament from afar and spurred on their horses. When they were near the place from whence the cries came, a raven circled over them and cawed as in foreboding. But the men had no notion that the ominous cawing was addressed to them. They watched the raven as it disappeared behind the tree-tops, and when they looked down to the ground they saw the up-rooted tree with an extremely beautiful girl tied to it.

"Help me, good people, help", called Šárka weeping, and the men believed her tears and moans.

They all jumped from their horses and Ctirad himself cut through her bonds. Šárka fell at Ctirad's feet and pretended gratitude. Ctirad was touched and, lifting her to her feet, asked her what had happened and who had bound her.

"Oh Sir," said Šárka, "I was out hunting with my father and his train, and when I was chasing a doe I became separated from the others and I got lost. At last I came out of the wood onto this path, and I took it joyfully, because I heard horses neighing ahead of me. I thought they were the horses of my father's company. But I was wrong. I came upon a bunch of girls from Děvín. Those cruel creatures took me prisoner and bound me till the straps bit into my skin. They mocked me for not having gone with them to Děvín earlier, for staying with my old father. When I wept, they laughed all the more. Perhaps the heat and the mead they had drunk had gone to their heads. But as soon as they heard the clatter of horses' hoofs, they were afraid it was my father and his men returning. They left me bound here and hastily mounted their horses. Look, in their haste they even forgot their jug of mead."

"Fancy," Ctirad and his people were surprised, "mead from the maidens' castle. I wonder what it tastes like?"

Ctirad tried the mead, and his men did too, and they liked it. It was not any ordinary mead. Vlasta, the maidens' commander, had bewitched it. Whoever drank of it once became drowsy, he who drank twice could not hold his sword, and he who drank of it three times fell to the ground, overcome with sleep.

The men of Ctirad's retinue did not restrain themselves and they drank once, they drank twice and three times, and lay down in the forest grass that was silky as a maiden's tresses. They fell asleep and dreamt of victory over Děvín.

Ctirad drank twice and felt himself to be weak and torpid. Šárka took the horn from her neck and said with a smile:

"Sir, I am too weak after what I have suffered. But perhaps you could blow this horn. If my father is somewhere in the forest with his company, he will hurry here as soon as he hears the sound of this well-known horn."

Ctirad grasped the horn and blew it with the last of his strength. That was the sign the girls hidden in the thickets were waiting for. They leapt on their horses, rode like the wind, and surrounded Ctirad, Šárka and the sleeping men. The enchanted drink had taken Ctirad's strength. He soon gave in. The girls bound him and Šárka, whose bonds he had so lately cut, helped them to do it. The girls killed Ctirad's company on the spot. Not a man was able

31

to raise himself from the grass and all of them went from sleep straight into death. Then the girls led Ctirad to Děvín between their horses like a slave who had escaped his master. The scene of this deceit and betrayal is still called Šárka today and it is said that for a long time the laughter and howling of evil spirits could be heard there, delighting over human perfidy.

The fighting girls erected a wheel in front of Děvín, into which they entwined the tortured Ctirad. The men of Vyšehrad saw their cruel work and counted the days that separated them from the moment of revenge. The time was ripening, the numbers of spears, swords, shields, bows and arrows grew like spring wheat. Evil begat weapons and weapons were preparing to beget evil.

Vlasta knew of the arming at Vyšehrad, but she was so sure of her power that she merely smiled at the men's doings. However Ctirad's death had armed the men better than smiths and armourers.

They did not even wait for the day of revenge, which was to be decided by Prince Přemysl, but grief and anger over Ctirad's slaying drove them into the forests, where they attacked bands of the Děvín amazons and slaughtered them without mercy.

As soon as news of this was brought to Vlasta she was seized by such fury as a she-bear that has lost her cubs. She rushed into the Děvín courtyard and ordered an assault on Vyšehrad that would rock it to its foundations.

The men saw the approaching army of women from the battlements and rode out to meet it. Both sides spurred their horses, both sides were spoiling for the fight.

A terrible battle broke out, such as had never been seen or heard of, for a father was opposed by his daughter, a brother by his sister and a husband by his wife. The struggle knew no mercy, anyone who hesitated, if only for a moment, paid for their delay with their lives. The most reckless of all was Vlasta. She darted forward on her horse, without a glance to right or left, as if she wanted to reach the gates of Vyšehrad and destroy the castle single-handed. Not one of the maidens could keep up with her. Too late Vlasta realized that she had got too far from her band. Seven young men surrounded her, closed in upon her, and seven knives ended her life.

Confusion reigned in the band of girls. Many of them turned their horses back to Děvín, but the men followed them right into the castle courtyard.

There fell Vlasta's counsellors, and there too fell the beauties who had lured men into snares with cunning, even the skilful archeresses fell. The earth was soaked with blood as it is with rain in the days of autumn. Šárka too perished in the Děvín courtyard, at the hand of Ctirad's son.

Prince Přemysl decreed that the maidens' castle should be set on fire and destroyed. The castle died with its amazons.

Děvín burned long into the night and the conflagration could be seen over the whole land. Now even sceptics could see that those who help themselves to victory through treachery unerringly prepare their own defeat.

KARLŠTEJN

Anyone who made his way, around the middle of the 14th
century, during the reign of the Bohemian king and Roman emperor Charles IV., south of Prague against the flow
of the Berounka river, saw the building site of an extensive castle. In the forests along the Berounka Matyáš of
Arras was building the castle of Karlštejn on a rocky cliff
with a great number of workers. It was a treasury castle, its walls were to protect the Bohemian and the German coronation jewels, the emblems of imperial power
and the treasures that the sovereign had collected. These
treasures included the crown of St. Charles and the sword
that legend says was given him by an angel. The most resplendent hall of the whole castle was the chapel of the
Holy Rood. Its walls were faced with pure gold set with
precious stones and precious pictures, and the flames of
glowing candles were reflected in the shining walls. There
was such a brightness in the chapel as if the sun had its
home in it and set out from there on its heavenly pilgrim-
age. The castle and its precious jewels were guarded by
forty-two knights, and it was guarded too by firm ramparts
and a steep slope. The emperor used to come here to
pray in strict isolation. Karlštejn became for him what
Zbraslav was for some of the Přemyslides: a place of calm,
rest and concentration—and contentment too.

Karlštejn

It is said that the greatest Bohemian king and Roman Emperor Charles IV., called by Czechs the Father of his Country, was, like all those who do good deeds, much hated by devils...

The great works that were built during the reign of this prodigy amongst kings are innumerable, and after more than six centuries they bear witness to his magnanimity and sense of beauty. One of the best-known buildings that he left in his beloved Bohemian kingdom is Karlštejn Castle, considered to be the most beautiful Czech castle and one of the most imposing castles in Europe.

This magnificent seat was intended not only as an invulnerable hiding place for the royal jewels, it was also a shelter in which the Bohemian king found leisure and drew strength to fulfil new dreams.

But the devils who try to devastate all good intentions, did not leave the emperor in peace even in Karlštejn. It is said that two of them settled down in the Karlštejn forest.

In those days people were afraid to travel, they were afraid even to approach the new castle.

Anyone who entered the deep Karlštejn woods was attacked. The devils attacked them like cats pouncing on mice, took all their possessions and again hid in their holes in the cliffs.

In those days people were terrified of every rustle in the woods, every crackle, every breath—the malicious devils lay in wait for their prey day and night.

So King Charles offered a big reward to anyone who would drive the devils from his castle.

But fear of the powers of hell was too strong, no one came to claim the reward.

Till one day...

"Master Burgrave, Sir, I'll get the better of those fiends of hell," was uttered in the Burgrave's chamber.

The Karlštejn burgrave looked up in amazement...

It was no knight standing before him, no warrior, no brave man steeled in battle. It was just a boy, in an ordinary farmer's smock, a shepherd who grazed his sheep on the slopes of Karlštejn...

"You?"

The burgrave laughed.

But the boy nodded boldly.

"You want to engage in a fight with devils that not even the bravest knights in the kingdom have dared to undertake?"

"All I need are two sacks of peas and two horses— if you give me those I promise you I'll manage the devils. Where a sword does not help a clever head can..."

So the burgrave ordered that the shepherd should be brought two well-built horses and he had two sacks of salted peas loaded onto them... He was sorry for the lad, he already saw him torn to pieces amongst the Karlštejn cliffs.

The shepherd rode into the forest.

He rode slowly between the vast trees, the horses neighed nervously, they could feel the hellish fiends.

Then the shepherd stopped his horse and let only the horse loaded with the sacks of peas go on, himself waiting behind.

What he had expected happened. The devils saw the horse with the two sacks of peas trotting on alone and caught hold of its bridle. They took down the sacks and looked inquisitively inside. They started hungrily on the peas, cramming them into their mouths with both hands, seemingly unable to get enough of them. They didn't stop till both sacks were empty.

As soon as they finished eating they became terribly thirsty.

It looked as though the whole river Berounka would not be enough to quench their thirst.

They drank and drank. As soon as they'd finished the peas steeped in the water began to swell.

The devils roared in pain, they experienced such torture as if the pain of all those they had harmed had come back to them.

After a moment of immeasurable suffering the devils burst.

The shepherd then dared to go after them on the other horse. He dismounted, crept up to their dead bodies, and saw for himself that he had succeeded in exterminating the devils.

He jumped on his horse and rode triumphantly to Karlštejn.

Even from a distance he waved and called that the castle was freed from the forces of hell...

No one need any longer be afraid to travel in the Karlštejn woods.

The Bohemian king welcomed the shepherd joyfully. He made him the Karlštejn page and rewarded him royally.

Ever since that time the devils have left the Karlštejn forest in peace.

And the great king could continue to dream and to build.

Křivoklát

KŘIVOKLÁT

NIGHTINGALES AT KŘIVOKLÁT

The young Prince Charles, who was in the future to become the greatest Bohemian king and Roman emperor, Charles IV., spent some time in exile, together with his wife, a French princess, at Křivoklát castle.

His father, the Bohemian King John of Luxemburg, believed the slanderers who said his son wanted to take the throne from him.

He decided quickly, and exiled the successor to Křivoklát castle. There he was to live, in the midst of the forest, until John of Luxemburg changed his mind.

Blanche de Valois, the graceful French princess, sister to the French king, had to live with her husband in the remote castle.

The French princess and the Bohemian prince were in love with one another, yet they found their exile hard to bear. Exchanging court life that they were both used to, for a castle lost in the woods had a sad effect on the young girl, she longed for the lively world.

Here the days were measured by the sun's rising from the forest and setting over it, instead of a ruler's duties and pastimes. Nostalgia breakfasted, lunched and supped with Charles's young wife, Blanche de Valois. She was homesick.

She gazed from the tower at the boundless woods, she listened to the silence. She was used to life at the great royal courts, to dances, music...

She gazed from the tower into the dark skies and remembered her distant home. She had left all her relations, her friends and dear ones, and found herself exiled in an unknown country, whose customs and language she did not know...

The princess languished, her grief grew day by day. She looked hopelessly from the castle windows to the horizon, her home was beyond so many horizons...

And it is said that Charles saw her homesickness and sadness, and thought how he could give her pleasure. He was torn from his thoughts by the pure, ringing voice of a bird. Charles smiled. He ordered his servants to go round all the known bird-catchers far and wide, all those who caught songbirds in nets or with birdlime. They were to buy songbirds from them, especially nightingales. The servants brought back cages full of them. On Charles's order they were to take the cages full of birds into the thickets and among the saplings that climbed the slopes below Křivoklát. There amongst the green boughs, along the path leading from the side gate of the castle, they opened the cages and released all the songsters.

Blanche would often go out onto the path down to the stream. One day birdsong surprised her on her usual walk. Every branch, every bush was singing. Never before had so much song welcomed Blanche de Valois on the slopes of Křivoklát. It is said that the singing brought her comfort in her exile. The nightingales sang in the evening and late into the night, their voices rose to the castle windows and entered into the castle, banishing sad night thoughts.

The young prince had not kept the songbirds in their cages, but he and his wife were caged in Křivoklát, prisoners, like caged birds. The nightingales sang to them of freedom...

King John's young son made a calm path of nightingales for his wife Blanche, but for himself there was a restless lot. He was soon reconciled with his father and then we see him on campaigns and journeys in Poland, Hungary, Lithuania, Italy... In battles and in state negotiations.

The nightingales' path in Křivoklát was a short happy path in the French princess's path of life.

She left this world young, beautiful, in love...

As fairies leave the world in story books.

She died so young.

She did not live to wear the royal or imperial crown at her husband's side.

What did she leave behind?

Just her name.

Blanche de Valois.

Just a legend.

And the path on the slopes below Křivoklát, on which the princess came out from the side gate and which she herself called "the nightingales' path".

Perhaps you too may hear a nightingale sing there.

And perhaps it will sing that same song that the unhappy Princess Blanche heard on these slopes more than six centuries ago.

In times that were favourable to alchemists the adventurous Englishman, Edward Kelley, came from England, via the court of the Polish king, to the Prague imperial court. His life was shrouded in a mysterious mist, which he knew how to use to his own advantage. No one at the court knew that Kelley, who proclaimed himself an alchemist, was a runaway chemist and notary with a very strange past. Kelley, who was full of ideas, plans and dreams, won over the emperor at once with his inflammable eloquence. He was allowed to set up an alchemist's workshop in the house that was later to be called Faust's House. And there too he lived contentedly with his wife and step-daughter, later famous as the English poetess Vestonová.

The emperor urged the alchemist to hasten with his experiments. He wanted results. And Kelley announced that he had succeeded in producing gold, and that he would demonstrate his discovery to the emperor. He invited the sovereign to his alchemist's workshop in Faust's House, so that he should himself be present.

The emperor had his experience of swindling alchemists. So he had the whole room where the experiment was to be made carefully searched. But nowhere was there even a scrap of gold dust. And the alchemist Kelley had to let himself be searched too, to see whether he was not hiding a bit of gold on him, that he would drop into the jar at the critical moment. Finally the courtiers could assure the emperor that there was not a single grain of gold in the whole room.

And only then, legend says, did Kelley order an enormous chest to be brought into the workshop, full of alchemists' aids, instruments and all sorts of powders and liquids. Every instrument, every ingredient was carefully examined to see whether it did not hide gold. The emperor himself placed the necessary substances, according to the alchemist's instructions, into the jar, which he carefully examined beforehand, to see if it hadn't got a false bottom. Then the jar was closed in the emperor's presence and placed over the fire.

Then the emperor and the courtiers left the room. Now Kelley called up helpful spirits. He called them up alone, because spirits are said to be shy and cannot bear the presence of strangers. Then he left the room himself and the emperor had the door sealed.

An hour passed. The emperor ordered the door to be unsealed and with his own hand opened the jar over the fireplace. And behold—in the jar gold glittered with a yellow light. What joy! What enthusiasm! There would be no more worries as to where to find more and more gold to buy precious objects for the emperor's collections.

The happy emperor knighted the English adventurer and waited for more gold. But more gold allowed itself to be waited for. Kelley made excuses and extensive preparations for a new experiment and especially—demanded more and more money.

After a while people began to whisper amongst themselves that the chest that had been brought into the alchemist's workshop had a false bottom. It was said that the alchemist's helper had hidden in the close quarters of the chest with a pouch of grains of gold. It would have been enough for him to get out of the chest at a certain moment, pour the golden grains into the jar and hide himself again in the chest.

The golden knight Kelley grew rich on the emperor's trust. His property increased, he owned houses and estates. But hardly had he reached the peak of his glory—when he came to a precipice.

When the short-tempered Kelley killed one of the emperor's courtiers in an argument, the emperor's favour came to an end. Kelley realised that his beautiful days were over, and he wanted to escape. He saddled his horse and threw into a sack all that came to hand that was most precious. How small the sack was, and how great the riches that he had to leave behind!

He mounted his horse and relied on the darkness of night. He hoped that no one would recognize him and that he could get past the guard. There were still a few moments of hope.

He galloped through the dark, narrow, little streets, but then his way was blocked by horsemen who were already searching for him. He fell into their hands.

As long as the emperor showed his alchemist favour no one dared speak ill of the golden knight. But no sooner did the emperor begin to be angry with him, than everyone knew something against the adventurous alchemist. So numerous were the reports of his swindles that the emperor had him taken to Křivoklát and imprisoned there. In Křivoklát, in a tower named Huderka, he could reflect in silence and loneliness on the path to success that he had climbed so steeply only to fall so suddenly.

Kelley tried to escape from the Křivoklát tower. He cleverly plaited a rope from everything he could get hold of that seemed at all suitable. When the rope was long enough he tied it, one starless night, to the grating of his prison window. He managed to squeeze through the little window himself, to freedom. He let himself down, but the rope was frail, it wouldn't bear him and broke. Kelley fell into the depths, bruised himself and broke his leg.

Later the crippled alchemist was released from prison. But before long he was imprisoned again in the town of Most. And there, it is said, he killed himself in desperation.

KOKOŘÍN

THE PHANTOMS OF KOKOŘÍN

It is said that there are two ancient phantoms living in Kokořín castle.

The first is a shining girl. A strange apparition that floats over the moat, appears in the tower gallery, dances with fluttering skirts round and round the castle.

The other is a wild huntsman. He appears more often, and he does so, as is the custom with phantoms, when the clock strikes midnight...

The darkness is torn by the neighing of a horse. A pack of hounds starts barking. Flames flicker from the dogs' mouths, the pack rushes down the Kokořín cliffs and ravines and after them rides the wild huntsman.

A black figure on a black horse, carved out of the darkness, charges after the pack and hunts game with a cross-bow.

When the hunt ends he goes back, disappearing behind the ramparts of Kokořín.

But neither he nor his horse and dogs want to go back.

And where do they go? To hell?

The dogs that must leave this world and disappear again into the unknown howl desperately, the horse rears and the huntsman screams piteously.

But they cannot save themselves. They have to go, and can return only briefly.

Nobody knows why the mysterious rider emerges, what purpose or curse drives him into this world.

Even though his coming is terrifying, it has never happened that the black rider harmed anyone. He may even give a rich reward to someone who is without hope—he once hung a pouch of golden coins on the branch of a tree for a poor woodcutter...

Was that money that he was miserly with during his lifetime, refusing it to the needy?

Kokořín

Do misers long to give away their fortunes after death?

And who is the girl who wanders here? Who harmed her when she was alive, or whom did she harm?

The white girl and the black rider tread their unending road and bear with them some unknown guilt.

They want to shake it off.

But only the living can get rid of their guilt.

As long as they are alive.

THE PETROVSKÝ BAND

The Thirty Years' War had ended. Many of the burnt-out villages were overgrown with grass and bushes. Many once lively paths were lost in the green of the forest. Weeds grew out of the rubble of city houses and the ruined walls were inhabited by lizards. Nobody disturbed them. The fields gave birth to nettles and the deserted cow-sheds were silent.

Only slowly did people return to the empty settlements. In places where hundreds of people had lived before, hardly several dozen of them met after the war. Only few towns and villages survived the long warring.

The war had left destruction behind it, and also soldiers no longer used to the plough. And there were many deserters from both native and foreign armies, discharged men and armed companies, and all of them had got to know an easier life. And there were many people too who had lost everything. Evil times had taught them crime. No one who set out in the morning knew whether he would reach his destination alive and well. Hiding in the forests and ruins were men into whose hands war had pressed weapons and peace had not taken them away. It was said that in those evil days the deserted Kokořín castle had become the headquarters of a band of brigands. The name of their chief was Petrovský. He was a chief who was feared above all others and was famous for his thieving raids and for his bravery. So it became the custom at that time to call brigands, wherever they appeared in Bohemia, the Petrovský band.

The Petrovský band would set out from the old Kokořín castle through secret underground passages to steal. And then again they would disappear with rich spoils into the mouths of passages that were hidden among the bracken and thickets, as though the earth had swallowed them.

One night the Petrovský band set out to rob a mill not far from Mělník. The thieves were favoured by thick darkness, and a steady light rain erased all trace of them. In the hiss of the rain and covered by darkness they reached the courtyard, and they would certainly have killed everyone in the mill who tried to stop them. But the old miller's help slept lightly, he heard the skulking robbers' steps and woke up the mill labourers. A bitter fight broke out.

The Petrovský band had to retreat to the forest. They considered their unsuccessful attack to be a disgrace to their robbers' craft and their chief swore revenge.

Some days later a handsomely dressed gentleman appeared at the mill, his fingers were all rings and his mouth all pleasant speech. He said he came from Mělník, owned a house there and also a vineyard beyond the town. The trusting miller believed this gentleman. He did not even mind that he paid marked attention to his daughter Liduška. The miller and his wife entertained the rich stranger and allowed Liduška to go for a walk with him along the mill-race.

The gentleman talked and talked and he and Liduška got further and further from the mill. They reached the edge of the forest. And then the saplings were pushed aside and the stubbly faces of the robbers appeared. Liduška did not even have time to scream for help. Someone's hand closed her mouth, someone bound her arms and—goodbye freedom. The robbers carried off Liduška though the forest and amongst the thickets descended into one of the secret underground passages. They took Liduška along it to Kokořín.

Now Liduška recognized the rich strange gentleman. He stood before her and laughed at how successful his abduction had been. It was the brigand chief himself, Petrovský. Liduška fainted in fright.

When she awoke she was lying in the cellars of Kokořín castle. In the corner an old hag was cooking something for the robbers' supper. Voices could be heard. The robbers were consulting on what to do with Liduška. Liduška fainted again in horror.

She only came to in the night. Loud breathing could be heard from the next-door cellar. The robbers had eaten and drunk and now were contentedly sleeping it off. Only the old woman was not asleep. She was sitting by the fireplace and raking out the cinders.

Liduška started crying.

"Grannie," she begged the old woman softly, "for God's sake, help me. I have done no harm to anyone and yet I am to be punished."

The old woman nodded her head for a while and then she sighed:

"How many times have I wanted to save someone, yet I have never saved anybody. I was afraid for my life. But now, girlie, I am so old that I fear for my life no longer. You are the first, and also probably the last, for whom I shall do a good deed."

The old woman took a knife and cut Liduška's bonds. She poured some peas into her apron and said:

"When you go out into the forest, sprinkle the path with peas so that you can find the way back. You will come back, and you will not come alone."

Then the old woman took Liduška into a secret passage, lit a torch for her so that she could see her way, and told her which way to go when she got into the forest. Liduška thanked her and, her heart in her mouth, hurried along the passage with the flickering torch to reach the forest as soon as she could.

The torch was burning down when Liduška came out of the passage into the fresh air. The stars and the moon greeted her through the tree-tops. She ran down the hill and followed the stream against the current until the walls of her own dear mill shone white in the moonlight before her.

At home they had mourned her. As soon as she appeared amongst them, alive and well, joy took the place of weeping. She had to tell everyone how it had all happened.

Next day the miller went to Mělník and came back with armed neighbours. They and the mill labourers all set forth into the forest. The scattered peas led them to the mouth of the secret passage, and along the passage

51

they got right into the robbers' den in Kokořín.

The surprised robbers tried to find their weapons, they wanted to resist, but they did not manage to shoot from a single pistol or slash with a sword. All of them were taken prisoner and bound. Even their famous chief Petrovský.

When they reached Mělník with them, people came running from all sides to look at them. The name, the Petrovský band, went from mouth to mouth. That name was to fly even over centuries and find its way into storybooks.

Another Petrovský band settled in the deserted castle Houska. It was led by the Swedish commander Oront. He didn't want to go home to Sweden. He stole in Bohemia as a soldier, and when the war ended he continued in the same craft. The people of Mělník had the greatest trouble with him. He would attack their carriages on the forest paths, take their baggage, he ambushed travellers and knew no mercy. It was announced in Mělník that whoever would rid the region of Oront the brigand would receive one hundred tolars.

The gamekeeper Jiranda of Stránka heard of this. Jiranda was a strong fellow, at least a head taller than other gamekeepers. He went to Olešnice to see his friend, gamekeeper Mazanec. They agreed that they would go together to Houska castle and would settle with the brigand Oront once and for all.

It was said that the bullet that would kill Oront had never yet been made. He had been through gunfire so many times and no shot had ever touched him.

A blacksmith from Střezivojice helped the bold gamekeepers. He knew how to make magic bullets that would hit even the invulnerable. At midnight on a day when the dark side of the moon was turned to the earth the blacksmith made the bullet, and with it he settled Oront's fate.

The next thing that had to be done was to choose who should fire the bullet. The two gamekeepers made trials to see which of them was the better shot. They competed with one another, but do what they would, they were always both winners. Finally Jiranda took a burning candle

52

out into the dark and stood it on the stump of a tree.

"The one to hit the candle-flame is the victor," said Jiranda, "and he may aim his gun at Oront."

Twice both gamekeepers shot out the light of the candle. But the third time Jiranda's firm hand wavered and he missed the target. His friend Mazanec did not miss the target even for the third time.

So the gamekeeper Mazanec got the magic bullet.

Before dawn the next day the two gamekeepers set out for the brigand Oront's castle. They took a few other friends with them, each of whom carried two or three guns and ropes and nails, to help them get inside the castle.

A deserted old smithy with a broken roof stood near the castle. And in that smithy the gamekeepers hid. Mazanec climbed up to the loft and among the holes in the roof found an opening between the shingles through which he pushed his gun. The barrel pointed straight at the windows of the castle dining-room, where the brigand Oront both ate and slept.

As soon as night took the place of daylight gamekeeper Jiranda climbed the cliff opposite the castle and began calling: "Oront, Oront!"

The brigand appeared in the dining-room window and shouted angrily: "Who wants what of me?"

"You'll find out at once," Jiranda replied.

At that moment a shot rang out and the magic bullet shot from Mazanec's gun flew through the air and hit Oront right in the middle of his forehead. Oront just had time to call: "Quick, quick, hurry up, my black hen!"

But death was quicker than the brigand's spell. Not even the devil had time to rush to his aid. Oront, who had killed so many people, was at last killed himself.

The Petrovský band in the castle lost their certainty when their leader fell. The gamekeepers and their friends fired all the guns they had brought, as if the whole army were closing in. While some were shooting, others hammered in nails, fastened ropes and climbed into the castle. In the end the Petrovský band, confused by the shouts and the shooting, surrendered. It is said there were ten of them. The gamekeepers bound them and took them to Mělník. Mazanec and Jiranda got the promised one hundred tolars.

The story goes that Mazanec never shot again from the gun he had fired at Oront. He hung it up on a nail and for long it was kept in his family as a memorial. With the gun the gamekeeper's descendents would also pass on one of the tolars. But in time the gun was lost and even the last tolar rolled away somewhere at last.

All that was left were legends about the Petrovský band.

Konopiště

KONOPIŠTĚ

THE ARCHDUKE AND DRAGONS

The time of legends is not over.

Stories come into being even in modern times.

The name of the best known lord of Konopiště, archduke Francis Ferdinand d'Este, is often spoken in psychiatric contexts. Especially his sinister passion is mentioned—his passion for killing. He killed thousands and thousands of animals when out hunting, not for the joy of the hunt. He dealt out death for the delight of killing. He was not a huntsman, even his contemporaries thought of him as a butcher.

Like many of the Habsburgs he was pathologically cruel—when he flew into a rage he did not hesitate to raise a whip or a sword against those around him...

The collection of St. Georges that this "highborn butcher" accumulated at Konopiště castle became renowned and outlived him. The people of his time could not understand why the archduke collected so passionately every kind of representation of St. George fighting the dragon. Banners, gravestones, coins, pipes... everything that bore a picture of St. George was sent to Konopiště to swell the strange collection of this eccentric magnate.

But the archduke did not collect his Georges and dragons without reason.

He had a great dream. He had heard that the English King George collected images of his namesake and patron saint. He was determined that not the king of England but he would have the biggest collection of St. Georges in the world.

And so ever more hundreds and hundreds of objects with the motif of the dragon-killer found their way to Konopiště castle.

The archduke spent huge sums of money on this collection, which contained works of art beside worthless trash... he ordered more and still more objects to be sent to the castle.

It seemed he was interested in nothing but their number.

A crazy dream...

One day the archduke would invite the English king to shoot partridges at Konopiště, and that day the English king would be astounded when he saw that it was not he who had the biggest collection of St. Georges in the world, but d'Este.

They never met at Konopiště.

The archduke was shot and the English king entered the war against the Austrian empire.

Only the collection of St. Georges remained in memory of a conceited longing...

The archduke amassed thousands of dragons—and he did not realize that people carry the worst dragons in their hearts, a great evil that may sometimes be invisible even to themselves.

Knowing how to drive out the dragon from one's own heart is a great art.

Wars arise from small causes that build up into big reasons...

It is hard to say what the real reason was for this or that war.

The First World War, that brought misery to Europe for four years, also had many reasons.

But two places that contributed towards it are known. The first of them, Sarajevo, is known even to schoolchildren, the second is known to few people. In Sarajevo the successor to the Austro-Hungarian throne, lord of Konopiště, archduke Francis Ferdinand d'Este, was killed. This assassination is considered to be the excuse for the beginning of the First World War.

Yet this beginning also had its beginning...

On 12th June 1914 the German emperor came to Konopiště castle to agree on an alliance of war with the archduke.

The archduke's wife was a Czech countess, Sofie Chotek. He had married her after a long romantic relationship, when he had to struggle with the Austrian court. He had his own way, instead of a royal bride he married the woman he wanted... but he had to pay for it.

He remained successor to the throne even after his wedding, but it was a morganatic marriage, and the children of his marriage with the Czech countess would have had no claim to rule the Austrian empire.

And the German emperor, who lusted for war, made use of just this fact: he promised to see that the archduke's children should gain the right of inheritance... even that they should win still other thrones, those that he would conquer in war.

The archduke was willing to be persuaded.

Perhaps there had never before been more secret negotiations in the whole of Austria than those between the archduke and the emperor in Konopiště, negotiations held behind the Austrian ruler's back. He did not agree with the German plans for a European war.

The archduke knew that he would have to wait till the old Austrian emperor died, and then he would become emperor... He knew that the emperor had no love for him, and that if the emperor's only son, Prince Rudolph, did not commit suicide, the Austrian emperor would never agree to see the archduke on the throne...

The castle was extremely well guarded during these supersecret talks... The doors were lined with big mattresses, so that not a single sentence should go further than to the ears of the two who were discussing ways and means.

So anxious were they that those sentences should be secret.

Evil always has to be kept the most secret.

The archduke heeded no warnings and went to Sarajevo, where both he and his wife were assassinated. But the plan that he and the German emperor had thought up went into effect without him...

Years passed...

The war that was planned here had broken out, brought endless suffering, caused unimaginable damage and ended.

Those who had caused it had lost their power, respect, their lives...

Indeed the Austrian empire, one of the mightiest in Europe, came to an end in this war.

All that remained were stories...

A story about the castle where two people agreed on a great evil, two people decided on the misery and suffering of whole nations...

How many millions of people died, were wounded, broken-hearted, because of the sentences that two madmen exchanged in the rooms of a Czech castle.

They supposed they had the fate of the world in their hands.

While not even their own fate was within their power.

ŠTERNBERK

THE SECRET OF ŠTERNBERK CASTLE

It is said that Šternberk castle, seat of the lords of "the eight-pointed star" (as the famous Czech noble family of Šternberks is called), hides a great treasure, that no one throughout the centuries has yet managed to find.

Once the lord of the castle gave his burgrave Hynek into safe keeping a large chest with a treasure of golden coins...

"Burgrave," he said, "I am going to Vienna, and this money gives me anxiety. I do not know where to hide it. Look after it for me, guard it till I come back."

When the lord of the castle had departed, the burgrave felt very much afraid. Where should he hide the treasure? How could he guard it?

Day and night the burgrave thought about the money and how he could best look after it, so that he could give it back to his master.

There were robbers skulking around the castle...

And inside the castle—so many people he could not trust.

Since his master had left the burgrave did not know a moment's peace.

Until one night... He set out with the treasure from the chamber in which it was hidden, and laid it in an unknown place.

And then he only waited impatiently till his master should come home.

But then it happened that the burgrave became paralysed. He had a stroke and was unable to move or to speak. He was dying...

He tried desperately to inform the priest of something... but the priest did not understand. With the greatest effort the burgrave moved his rigid lips, he gave out incomprehensible sounds, tried with trembling fingers to

Šternberk

point somewhere... And people nodded as if they understood, just to pacify the burgrave. But they had no idea
what it was that Master Hynek wanted to tell them.

When the lord of the castle returned he ran at once
to see if the treasure was all right. But the treasure had
disappeared. The lord was told of the burgrave's death,
and of how he had tried so hard to pass on some informa-
tion...

They searched everywhere in the castle, tapped walls,
dug holes... but they did not discover the hiding-place of
the vast Šternberk treasure.

Maybe the treasure is still in the castle. It has waited
for centuries for the one who will discover it. And maybe
it will be one of the visitors who come to the castle
this year.

Kutná Hora

KUTNÁ HORA

HOW THE NAME KUTNÁ HORA ORIGINATED
(LITERALLY COWL HILL)

Impenetrable forest once covered the whole of this region, all the country around today's Kutná Hora was one big wood... There was one small castle over the valley of the Vrchlice river that guarded the whole area, and the rustling of the leaves on the trees was the only sound that broke the great silence...

And the lord of that part, Miroslav of Cimburk, summoned monks to come and clear the forest and found settlements.

Nobody believed that a town would grow here that would not only be one of the biggest in the whole kingdom of Bohemia, but would at the height of its fame be one of the richest towns in Europe and even rival Prague.

And the monks went into the deep forest and searched for a place where they could fell and uproot the trees, so that ears of corn would grow from ploughland in place of the great trunks of pines.

A monk named Antonín went in the year 1237 to the place where the church of All Saints towers today, but then only trees towered there, and beneath them stretched fragrant moss. The monk, tired from his long journey, lay down on the moss to rest.

And he had a dream.

Brother Antonín dreamed that he struck the ground with a hoe. And the sound it gave was not as if he had touched clay, but a bell.

And in his dream the monk dug on and on, and wherever he dug an immense radiance of silver rose to the surface. Everything was silver, the rocks, the trees, the roots...

A silvery dream...

Brother Antonín awoke from his silvery dream, but as if the dream was continuing, three silver rods were growing in front of him. He touched them cautiously, would they not dissolve under his fingers?

They did not dissolve, they really were rods of pure silver. The monk knelt down and gave thanks for the gift he had found.

He left his cowl in that place, so as to mark it, and hurried to the monastery to tell the brothers of his find as soon as might be.

In memory of the discoverer of silver, in memory of the cowl with which the monk marked the place, the settlement there was named Cowl Hill—Kutná Hora.

One of the most lucrative mines in the town was named Osel, which means donkey. And there was an old prophesy that was handed down in Kutná Hora from generation to generation:

As long as the donkey brays
Good fortune in Cowl Hill stays...

And the miners kept on taking silver out of Osel, as if its wealth was eternal. One generation of miners took the place of another, and "the donkey" kept on "braying", more and more veins of silver were discovered. And through those veins prosperity flowed into the town and into the Bohemian kingdom.

As long as the donkey brays...

One day the miners were digging a gallery very deep down, they had to descend further and further, as the metal was already exhausted at the higher levels.

They did not know that only a thin wall divided them from death. They ignored the hammering of the "little smiths", though it could be heard loudly...

A vast lake of underground water was waiting behind a thin layer of rock that became thinner with every hammer blow.

Tap, tap...

A single hammer blow was enough...

An immense wave burst out from the rock.

And the miners disappeared in the depths, swept away by the underground water.

As long as the donkey brays...

Everyone in the town remembered the ancient prophesy, and it sent shivers up their spines...

And the people of Kutná Hora hurried to the mine, they carried pots, pitchers, tubs to help the drowning mine. But the water in the mine kept on rising. Even though they tried for days on end to pump it out and carry it off, the underground lake slowly and irresistibly spread.

In 1554 the water reached "the donkey's head".

It happened on St. Matthew's Day.

And people gathered to look at "the donkey" that had "stopped braying".

And the water that drowned the mine floated away the fame of Kutná Hora - Cowl Hill...

The families of Kutná Hora amassed vast wealth. The patricians of the town grew rich from the silver mines and ruled unquestioned.

One of the town councillors of Kutná Hora was Jiří Ruthard, an extremely wealthy man. He had a beautiful and proud daughter. Every man longed to have her as his wife. But Rozina, as the girl was named, would have nothing to do with any of them. None of the suitors was good enough for her.

And it happened that the Austrian ruler Albrecht became jealous of the Bohemian King Wenceslas II. At that time Wenceslas was one of the most powerful rulers in Europe, being king not only of Bohemia but also of Poland and Hungary. And the Austrian ruler decided to go to war with three-fold King Wenceslas.

The main thing he wanted was to seize the Kutná Hora mines. For whoever owned the Kutná Hora mines could equip a powerful army and dare to do battle with anyone he chose.

So the Austrian ruler sent his messenger to Kutná Hora, a count, who was to persuade the people of Kutná Hora to surrender their town to him without a fight. And the clever ambassador began to pay court to the councillor's daughter.

Through the heart of the daughter I will reach the brain of the father, he reasoned. Rozina's heart was to be the key that would unlock the city gates.

And Rozina really did fall in love with the count.

But a scribe named Vít, who loved Rozina, was not going to submit to any rival. He challenged him to a duel and in the duel he killed him.

The miners of Kutná hora were determined to remain faithful to the Bohemian king, and they defended their town against the Austrian soldiers with all their might.

But Rozina Ruthard—hating her city—opened the gateway to the outlying part of the town, allowing the enemy army to enter part of the town and pillage it.

The councillor defended Kutná Hora. He had the stream from which the besieging soldiers drank poisoned. And with this, to use the modern phrase, chemical weapon, he weakened the enemy.

And the Bohemian king, who immediately came to his aid, drove the foreigners off.

The councillor, Rozina's father, passed sentence on his daughter. He condemned her to death.

And even though the king granted her mercy, she soon died. All she left behind her was a legend telling how a great unhappy love may grow into hatred.

Kutná Hora began to yield up its treasure.

There was a terrible hunger for silver.

The shafts crossed one another, intertwined, soon Kutná Hora was undermined in criss-cross fashion. And it seemed that the veins of silver were endless.

Thousands of miners worked in the narrow galleries, in the depths of the earth. Hammers and iron wedges—those were their tools. Day after day the galleries resounded with clang—clang, a million times and a million times more the hammers clanged on the iron wedges and inch by inch the passages in the cliffs grew longer...

The flickering light of miners' lamps replaced daylight for the miners, when they came out of the pits it was already night above ground.

When they came out of the pits the mines were not silent.

Clang, clang...

Clang...

Even when the galleries were empty the clanging went on. That was the gnomes of Kutná Hora, carrying on the work.

They called them "the little smiths"—tiny gnomes with long white beards.

The miners did their best to get on well with them. And it was worth it. Every year it was enough to bring the underground gnomes little red coats, and the gnomes knew how to repay these gifts with gratitude. They showed the miners the best places to burrow.

If they had not brought them the little red coats the gnomes would have avenged themselves. They could have led the miners so deep into the galleries that they got lost, they could have blown out the miners' lamps and left them underground in the dark, they could have told them to mine in places where there was no silver...

But on the whole the little smiths were kind-hearted.

They intimated by the clanging of their little hammers that the mine was going to be flooded, that there would be a disaster. They knocked loudly as a sign that the miners were to get out of the mine quickly and go up above ground.

Clang, clang...

Get out, get out...

In 1509 they gave loud signs to the miners, and it is said that even their little voices could be heard. But the miners went on working, water rushed into the mine and the miners were drowned.

Perhaps the gnomes still live today in the depths of the deserted mines, perhaps they still live in their castle hidden in the underground caves, in their shining silver castle wrought of pure silver...

MĚLNÍK

MĚLNÍK WINE

Since time immemorial vines have been cultivated on the sunny slopes of Mělník, since time immemorial the hill below Mělník castle has shone with the emerald stars of vine leaves.

It is told that the princess, St. Ludmila, grandmother of St. Wenceslas, cultivated vines above the confluence of the Vltava and the Elbe. Then the seat of the Pšovans stood here, the tribe whose last prince was Slavibor, father of St. Ludmila. She became the wife of the Bohemian Prince Bořivoj—and it was Bořivoj who brought this part of the country under the rule of the Prague House of the Přemyslides.

So right from the dawn of Czech history vines have been grown in this place, and they were cultivated by royal hands.

St. Ludmila made the grapes into wine that was used in the Christian holy mass.

And she brought her little grandson, Wenceslas, here to the slopes of Mělník, from the Mělník cliffs he looked at the lovely country he was one day to rule. On these slopes he helped his grandmother to grow vines.

For a thousand years vines have been grown in Mělník, and they give one of the best wines that come from Bohemia.

The Emperor and King Charles IV. had vines brought to Mělník from France—and he appreciated the wine from here and saw to its improvement.

Today vines are still grown on the same hills where St. Ludmila and St. Wenceslas cultivated them.

The Bohemian princely family of the lords of Lobkowicz, whom the castle and vineyards have belonged to for centuries, keeps up the famous wine-growing tradition at whose beginnings the Přemyslide saints stood.

Mělník

Whoever comes to Mělník can taste the delicious wine, the wine of Bohemian saints and kings, and can also visit the majestic cellars, in which the wine has been kept for centuries.

It is said that there is no wine in the world that is better for drinking toasts than the wine called after St. Ludmila.

It is told that treasure is hidden in the cliff under Mělník castle. The treasure is immense and it is hidden in the barrels used in Mělník to store wine. Deep in a secret place there are rows of barrels full of gold, silver and precious stones.

These barrels are ceaselessly guarded by a dog with fiery eyes.

For centuries people have searched for the Mělník treasure and for centuries they have been unable to find it.

It is told that the secret underground place opened itself to people just once, it opened during the reading of the Passion.

Then the entrance to this underground place opened like a gate.

The priests lit candles and went down into the cellarage, they walked through long, cold passages, hoping they would take the treasure and divide it amongst the poor and needy. With burning candles and prayers on their lips they descended deeper and deeper...

Then a great wind blew, a frosty, biting underground wind. The candles were extinguished at the moment when the priests glimpsed gold shining in the barrels in the flickering candle-light.

Only the dog's fiery eyes shone in the darkness...

The priests groped their way back through the darkness, but when they relit the candles and wanted to go down again, they could not find the path.

One day, they say, the treasure will be found. It will rise from the Mělník cliff by itself, and offer itself to the people of Mělník.

This will happen, according to the old prophesy, on the day that a great fire destroys the whole town. Even the day of that destruction is foretold in that prophesy. It will happen, it says, on the festival of Holy Trinity, and on that day the ancient and famous town of Mělník will be one great conflagration.

But from the money that the people of Mělník will get for the treasure they will be able to build their town again... and it will be still more beautiful.

It is said that in Mělník castle there lives a sprite who can help people to grow rich.

Once upon a time a scribe worked at the castle who drudged to make money for his wife. His wife forced him to write documents even at night, just so that he could earn even a little more and she could spend the money on finery.

Poor scribe.

After a time he could only drag himself about, weakened, underslept, emaciated, he just stumbled through the castle offices.

It was not that he earned little—but he was still poor, his wife spent all he earned. A rich man is not the one who earns well, but the one who manages well.

And his wife did not manage well, she only wanted more and more money.

One night the scribe fell asleep over the documents that he was copying, and when he woke he saw a little man standing on the desk in front of him, just by the ink-pot.

On his neck he had a pouch that jingled when he moved.

"Do you want some?" The sprite took some ducats out of the pouch.

The scribe pinched himself. I must still be asleep, he thought.

"Do you want some?"

Let me get some money at least in a dream, the scribe yearned, and even though he thought it was a dream, he nodded to the sprite to show he wanted his ducats.

And the sprite poured out ducats onto the desk.

"But don't tell anybody who gave them to you," he ordered.

And he disappeared.

For a while the scribe did not move, so that he should not wake up and put an end to that lovely dream that had brought him ducats.

At last he did move, he touched the ducats.

The did not vanish.

He put a ducat in his mouth and bit it, it was pure gold.

From that time on the sprite came to the scribe every night, and every night he brought him ducats. He carried so many of them that he was bent under their weight. And he always laid the ducats on the desk in front of the scribe.

He ordered that the scribe must keep silent as to who brought him those ducats.

And he disappeared.

The scribe gave his wife the money and she was well content. She received so much that even she could not spend it. But in the end she couldn't believe that the scribe was able to earn so much money through his work.

She insisted and insisted that he should tell her where the money came from.

The scribe resisted. He tried to think up something that would satisfy his wife, but she urged the scribe more and more.

In the end he told her.

Perhaps the sprite won't get to know, he comforted himself, after all, he can't know everything.

He waited impatiently for midnight, the time the sprite came to him.

Midnight struck...

With each stroke the scribe's anxiety grew, what if the sprite really had heard him, what if he didn't come that night.

But with the last stroke of the tower clock the sprite appeared

The scribe breathed a sign of relief.

But the sprite had no pouch of ducats on his neck as he usually had, they did not jingle sweetly at every step. He had angry sparks in his eyes and in his little hand he held a stick...

"You spoke what you should not have spoken," he shouted.

And he started to beat the scribe with his stick so hard and so deftly that the scribe could not protect himself from the blows and lost consciousness.

Next day they found the scribe lying by the desk in a faint, they brought him round and carried him home.

From then on the Mělník sprite did not bring a single farthing.

Sometimes its enough to say a word and the word alone brings wealth, but more often its enough to utter a careless word and one loses everything.

THE KNIGHTS OF MĚLNÍK

It is told that the Mělník cliff, on which the castle stands, hides a miraculous treasure within it, as a nutshell hides the kernel.

The kernel of Mělník cliff is a miraculous army.

A similar story is told of other places too. But rather more is known of the Mělník cliff, even the number of the miraculous warriors who wait within it is known. It is said that there are exactly three hundred knights within Mělník cliff.

They sit in underground caverns, their horses sleeping beside them. For long, long centuries they have been sleeping there... They are waiting.

From time to time one of the knights moves in his sleep, his precious weapon rings. From time to time a horse shifts in slumber, his horseshoe strikes the rock, as if he would awake at any moment and charge... From time to time a sword, grasped in a knight's sleeping hand, knocks on the rock with a silvery note, but then the whole cavern falls into an immense silence...

It is not yet time.

The Czech nation's worst moment has not yet come. When it does the hidden army will ride out...

It is told that the three hundred magic knights are commanded by the patron saint of the Czech Lands himself, Prince Wenceslas.

He too is reposing in the Mělník cliff.

He too is waiting.

When the command sounds the Mělník army will ride out from the cliff, which will crack open and retreat, the knights will ride out to help their enslaved land.

They will free it. And all over Bohemia a great peace will reign, prosperity, happiness...

Meanwhile the army sleeps.

It is waiting.

But one day the three hundred knights will ride out in shining armour, they will gallop out from the Mělník cliff, headed by the saint, for the last battle ever to be fought in Bohemia...

ŽEBRÁK

THE FIRST GUEST

(The name "Žebrák" means "beggar" and this is how it came by that name.)

Žebrák castle owes its origin to a lord of the family of Buzice, a powerful Czech family who ruled this region.

The castle is one of the oldest in the land, having been founded, it is said, as early as the 12th century...

And it is said that the knight who founded it was not rich, so he decided to build his castle on low ground where it was easier to transport the building materials. So he did not build on the surrounding high ground, though it seemed more suitable for the site of a castle.

The castle grew day by day and the knight considered what he should name it, but he could not hit on a suitable name.

Should it be called after his family?

It must have a noble sounding name... but what should it be?

The knight contemplated one name after another, but rejected each one.

It became high time to come to some decision as to what to call his castle.

And the knight decided.

He would name the castle after the first guest who entered the castle gateway when it was completed. If the knight could not think of a name, let it be determined by chance.

And the knight went up to the castle tower. He gazed round delightedly at the picturesque landscape...

But no one came along the road to the castle—no guest who would give his name to the nameless castle.

The knight grew sad... was his castle to remain unnamed?

Till one day... he saw on the road towards evening a black dot that gradually grew bigger... and the knight

Žebrák

saw that a young man was hurrying towards the castle. He wanted to reach the castle before it grew dark...

The knight came down from the tower and ran eagerly across the drawbridge to meet his guest.

The young man was poorly clothed, emaciated...

A wandering student.

A beggar.

He took out a lute from his ragged cloak and began to sing and play, he sang to beg for his supper and a night's rest...

He was surprised that the lord of the castle did not call his servants to throw him out or set the dogs on him, that he approached him in friendship, led him to the banqueting hall with a richly spread board, allowed him to sleep in a magnificent room, loaded him with gifts...

The knight knew why he paid him his respect.

The young man had become the godfather of the knight's castle.

And today it still bears his name. Today, even though the poor student and his lute have long since turned to dust, the castle is called Žebrák—the beggar.

Točník

TOČNÍK

THE SECRET OF TOČNÍK CASTLE

Žebrák castle was a favourite seat of the Father of the Country, Charles, King of Bohemia. Until 1351 he loved staying in this castle, but when his first-born son Wenceslas died there he ceased visiting the castle... King Wenceslas IV., another of Charles's sons, was also fond of this region. But the old Žebrák castle was not enough for him and he had a new castle built on Castle Hill.

But where should he find a name for it? There was a twisting, zig-zag path leading up to the castle. So people started to call the castle, because of the path, Točník— Zig-zag.

And it was one of the most splendid castles that ever stood in Bohemia, and indeed it was built by the Bohemian king, at that time he was amongst the richest kings in Europe. He had the castle furnished with every luxury. The huge halls with great hearths were ample for the large royal retinue, the stables hewn out of the cliff could house a hundred horses. This magnificent seat bore on its main gateway the coats of arms of all the countries that belonged to the Bohemian crown, that Wenceslas IV. ruled.

Točník was never conquered and destroyed by the enemy.

It became dilapidated, it was deserted.

During the Thirty Years' War people took refuge in the empty castle, to find there shelter from the Swedes.

But after that people only took away its stones to build with... who knows how many of the near-by houses would not be standing if it had not been for the castle, how many little homes the famous castle bears within its walls.

But one of the castle palaces, covered with a shingle roof, endured. No one destroyed that palace, no robber touched its roof.

The local people knew the old prophesy well.

"When Točník has a new roof, a white roof, a great evil will befall the kingdom of Bohemia."

And the time was inevitably approaching when the ancient prophesy was to be fulfilled.

There came one of the storms of the unhappy year 1914. A vast black cloud gathered over Točník castle. The lightning that flashed from it touched the castle roof and it burst into flame.

The old prophesy was fulfilled.

A new roof was put on the castle and, as was foreseen in the ominous prediction, it was white.

That was the moment of the outbreak of the First World War. And with the white roof of the castle great misfortune fell upon the Czech Lands.

There are stories of many secrets connected with the castle.

The castle lake hid strange fish—they were not covered with scales but with fur. And they were magical. They could miraculously escape fishermen. No net could hold them, they knew how to flee from it, to make themselves smaller and disappear through even the smallest hole. It was said that they were not fish, but that the souls of people lived in the lake whom a cruel lord of the castle had executed.

And it is said that a great treasure lies buried beneath the castle. For generations treasure-seekers from all around have come to the castle and tried to find the famous treasure. They never found it... But they dug up rubbish dumps in which they found huge quantities of bones left over from old royal feasts... and because rag and bone men bought the bones, people took sackfuls of at least the remains of royal feasts from the castle.

The treasure remained undiscovered.

It is still waiting in the depths of the hill. And it is guarded by the White Lady of Točník, who remembers so much and so much, even the time of the glory of one of the richest castles of central Europe, the time when the castle was filled with knights and hustle and bustle...

The White Lady of Točník glides silently around the castle.

To whom will she disclose where her treasure is?

And when?

Cheb

CHEB

TWO NIGHTS IN CHEB

It is a raw night in the last week of the month of February in the year sixteen hundred and thirty-four. Cheb is shrouded in darkness. Only where the soldiers of Valdštejn's company are billeted is there still light, and shouting and song resound. Here and there in the courtyard a fire burns and its flames illuminate the jutting bearded face of a mercenary. It is ruddy with cold and with drink. The aldermen of Cheb have delivered the first barrels of beer to Valdštejn's soldiers.

The Pachelbelov house in the square is not yet asleep either. The guard stamps up and down in front of the house, and in his upstairs room the Duke of Frýdlant, General Valdštejn, tosses on his bed. He is in cruel pain. On the journey from Plzeň to Cheb the whole procession had often had to stop. The general was carried on a stretcher slung between two strong and quiet horses. In spite of that he had felt every stone beneath their hoofs. Valdštejn is watching the flame of the candle on the table beside the bed. The more brightly the candle glows the quicker it burns down. Kepler's last horoscope had promised Valdštejn nothing pleasant for the beginning of this year. Valdštejn was losing the emperor's favour. And as yet it is only February.

Valdštejn, in a wave of pain, crushes the curtains around the bed in his fists. He would like to get his fists on all the officers who had betrayed him in the past weeks and gone over to the emperor's side. He would like to crush the emperor himself in his fists. The painful gout that had dogged Valdštejn for years would not allow him to sleep. And when the pain let up for a moment the helplessly prostrate duke was seized with anxiety as to what tomorrow would bring, what next week or next month.

90

In one of the little Cheb sidestreets Valdštejn's Colonel Butler was billeted. The ambitious Irishman Butler had invited the commander of the town, Colonel Gordon and Lieutenant Colonel Leslie to supper. Both these military gentlemen are Scotsmen. Valdštejn had many imperial soldiers recruited in England. All three officers were also worried about the future. Valdštejn is in disfavour with the emperor and a new commander had been appointed in his stead, Ottavio Piccolomini. The officers are supping, drinking and consulting.

Valdštejn tosses on the bed and consults with himself. He has always been used to give himself advice and obey it too.

Night slowly extinguishes the fires and the lights. Thick darkness hangs between the earth and the sky and does not admit a single star.

It is a night when a horse sees better than its rider. And the rider who is travelling from Plzeň to Cheb must not break his neck. He carries an important massage for the duke. Midnight is approaching and there is a frosty drizzle. Cheb's city gate is closed. Valdštejn sends a messenger to Leslie to order the gate to be opened and the rider brought to him. The rider, who has for long not left the saddle, mounts the stairs of the Pachelbelov house with a heavy wooden tread. He hands the prostrate Valdštejn a sealed letter, and while Valdštejn breaks the seal and reads the messenger secretly tries to get the stiff joints of his fingers moving in the warm room. Lieutenant Colonel Leslie, who has brought the rider, looks curiously at Valdštejn while he reads.

The general grimaces. But not in pain. He reads some sentences aloud, he shouts them, breaking them between his teeth. The emperor declares the former general of the imperial armies to be an outlaw. The emperor believed his councillors and General Piccolomini, who had denounced Valdštejn for allying himself with the Swedes and Saxons against the emperor.

Rage brings Valdštejn to a standing position even on his bed. He doesn's feel the pain and threatens the

emperor, he insults him. He does not realise in his parox-
ysm of fury that in the eyes of the careful and cunning
Scot he thus confirms his treachery.

The messenger forgets his numbness and stiffens with
fright at the general's ravings. His night ride through the
darkness had seemed to the tired horseman like a dismal
dream. Now it seems to him that he was carrying the devil
in that sealed letter.

A fresh wave of pain shuts Valdštejn's mouth. He falls
exhausted on the pillow. Very pale, he holds his breath.
The moment has come when it is as well to leave him.

Lieutenant Colonel Leslie brings his friends Butler and
Gordon the latest news. The emperor has declared Valdštejn an outlaw. An outlaw's life is worthless. The best
thing would be, says Leslie, to kill Valdštejn. All three of
them rely on the emperor's gratitude. Of course Valdštejn's faithful companions will also have to be killed—the
nobles Adam Erdmann Trčka, Illo and Kinský, who are
also in Cheb. The next day the commander of the town,
Gordon, invites all three noble gentlemen to supper at
Cheb castle for a Carneval celebration. The murderers
have already been hired and could dream of their reward.
The higher the rank of the conspirator, the greater the
reward he dreamt of.

And a second evening is falling over Cheb. For the
inhabitants of Cheb it is just another disagreeable February evening when Valdštejn's soldiers are roving about the
town. For some of the unwelcome guests in Cheb it was
the last night of their lives.

At dusk a carriage drives to Cheb castle with the nobles and their captain of cavalry. The banqueting hall is
prepared, it gives forth a pleasant warmth, and the fra-
grance of freshly baked meats comes from the kitchen.
The candle flames are reflected in the full goblets. The
wine does honour to the hosts. The meal takes place in
a calm and pleasant mood. But the murderers shift impatiently from foot to foot in hiding. One of them clasps a
musket till the barrel is warm in his hand, another grips a
sword, a third reaches to his side for a pistol or a dagger.

Everything is prepared. So let us begin in the name of the emperor's gratitude.

A dragoon bursts into the room and at the table Butler, Leslie and Gordon rise and shout the password to the dragoons:

"Long live Ferdinand!" In a brief, unequal fight the surprised nobles, the last who were loyal to Valdštejn, were killed together with their captain of cavalry and a servant who ran to their aid. Only Adam Erdmann Trčka got out of the building as far as the gate. His death blow caught him there.

The night still waited for Valdštejn's blood. Colonel Butler hurries with a small detachment of dragoons to the Pachelbelov house. They drove off the guard in front of the gate without difficulty. The designated murderer, Captain Deveroux, rushed up the stairs. He had broken his sword in the skirmish with the guard, so he had seized a partisan from the hand of the nearest soldier. It was a long weapon, like a spear or a halberd, sharp, intended for a fight on the battlefield. Now Deveroux charged with it into the sick Valdštejn's bedroom. On the way he killed Valdštejn's page.

The Duke of Frýdlant, now thanks to the emperor an outlaw, rose from his bed when he heard an unusual hubbub. That was how Deveroux caught him—amazed, in his night clothes, emaciated by his racking disease. Only the penetrating cold eyes still belonged to the commander. His body was quietly departing this life even without a murderer's help.

The captain hesitated before Valdštejn's gaze. For a moment he struggled with the remains of his respect for his commander, but then he shouted some curses, and strengthened by his own cries about Valdštejn, that rebellious beast, he raised his partisan to strike. A mighty blow of the blade hit Valdštejn right in the chest. The last victim of that night sank to the ground. Valdštejn was dead.

The emperor rewarded the duke's murderer with an estate in the Čáslav region, but Deveroux did not enjoy it for long. He died of the plague five years later in Prague.

Soon it began to be said that Valdštejn could find no peace in the grave. Every night, it was said, the duke's spirit would drive out of Cheb castle in a black coach. A two-in-hand of coal-black horses sets out from the castle gateway as soon as midnight strikes. Silently, as if they were stepping on feathers, the horses step high, drawing a coach in which the duke sits, pale, with a crimson stain on his snowy shirt. And woe unto him who meets his suspicious, frosty gaze.

The coach is accompanied on either side by horsemen, and behind the coach musketeers lead the duke's prisoner to his death. Who is it? Certainly someone whose crime against the duke was the greatest. One of the colonels, of the traitors and informers? The Duke of Frýdlant's wary eyes wander over the square, the coach drives away silently like a terrible wraith and dissolves in front of the Pachelbelov house. It is said that once there was a Cheb burgher, a scoffer, one of those who only believe in what he can drink, eat or touch. He laughed at his superstitious neighbours in the tavern in the square, and in proof of his intrepidity he went out exactly at midnight to the Pachelbelov house to wait till Valdštejn's ghost should come there with his train.

The Cheb beer, of which the burgher had drunk more than enough, had awakened his valour but also taken away his patience. Of course the duke in his coach and all that tattle was just so much tattle. Nothing was happening, he might as well go back to the tavern. Hardly had he decided to do so than a coach and horses came out of the street from the castle. Coal-black horses drew the coach in silence, as if a cloud passed by the burgher. Sitting in the coach was Valdštejn himself with a wound in his chest, and he gave the burgher a suspicious look. Horsemen grandly accompanied the ghostly coach in silence, as if they were woven of smoke. And now comes the detachment of musketeers. They are leading some captive to death. The moon comes out from behind a cloud and the captive lifts his face to heaven. Now the burgher recognized him. For it is he himself. He looks at himself as if in a mirror!

The terrified burgher does not even wait till the apparition dissolves. He runs stumbling back to his tavern. Well, what did you see? Tell us. The burgher gasps for breath, stutters, can scarcely get out a coherent sentence. Legend tells us he did not long survive his meeting with Valdštejn. Within a week he breathed his last.

But what use was his belated suspicion to Valdštejn, the generalissimo, when during his life he had believed treacherous colonels and generals?

LOKET

THE STRANGE STONE FROM LOKET CASTLE

For a long, long time people used to go and look at the strange stone that lay in the courtyard of Loket Castle. This longish stone glittered as if it were an alloy of gold and silver. And yet it was not. When it was struck it rang like a bell. And yet it was not bell-metal.

Even though the stone was not large, it could not be lifted by even the strongest man who attempted it. It was said around Loket that the only man who would be able to lift the stone was a man without sin—and as they never found such a man, no one ever lifted that stone...

And what is the legend about the Loket castle stone?

Once upon a time there lived in this castle a burgrave so cruel that his cruelty lives on in stories even after centuries. He had no mercy for any of the poor, the bondsmen were there to work and to pay. Otherwise they went to prison.

And at that time a poor, sick widow lived near the castle with a host of children. They had nothing to eat... the only thing they had was debts owing to the burgrave.

And the widow decided that she would go to him and beg for mercy. So one August Sunday she set out for Loket castle with a child that was crying from hunger in her arms.

She knelt down before the burgrave.

She begged him to have pity.

But the cruel burgrave was not won over either by the sick widow or the loud cries of the child...

Unless she paid him, he said, she would go to prison.

The widow burst into tears and again begged the cruel burgrave.

She might as well have begged a stone.

Loket

And then the kneeling woman threatened the burgrave and cried: "You have a heart of stone, so turn into a stone!"

The sky darkened, suddenly night fell on Loket.

Lightning flashed from the darkness.

And when the darkness passed a pit yawned beside the castle wall, stinking of sulphur, and on the bottom of the pit lay a glittering stone.

What a good place the world would be if everyone with a heart of stone ended like the burgrave of Loket...

Střekov

STŘEKOV

THE SACRIFICE

In ancient times belligerent hordes of Germans would penetrate into Bohemia on or along the river Elbe. Then with their booty they floated back up the river to their country in the north. The ruler of the Slav territory had a wooden castle built on the steep cliff over the Elbe, to ward off the attackers and guard the river.

After a time the wooden huts gave place to a stone castle. This guard castle was named Střekov.

But during the reign of Wenceslas IV. the castle ceased to be a guard. A knight named Kuba settled behind the battlements on the tall cliff. Kuba did not guard the lives and property of people in the surrounding country. Kuba took from people—their property and often their lives.

At that time a knightly tournament was being prepared at Bilina castle. News of it flew far and wide in all directions. Carpenters were already jointing stands in Bilina for the noble spectators and beams to fence off the arena.

The day came when the bare wood was covered with flowing materials, when knights and noble lords in tall hats sat on the benches, when the blare of trumpets and beat of drums mingled with the neighing of decorated horses. Bright-coloured pennants shone, belonging to the knights who had announced they would take part in the struggle. Suddenly a strange bustle and shouting spread amongst the knights. The knight Kuba of Střekov had appeared in their midst. Nobody wanted to stand beside him, nobody wanted to begin the ceremonial bowing until Sir Kuba had left the castle.

"Go back, Kuba, to where you came from," the young knight of Vrabinec advised him, "here we shall fight openly, face to face, and your custom is to fall on people from ambush."

Kuba left Bilina in ignominy and on the way to Střekov he swore a terrible revenge at every stone and at every tree.

The next day he got his armed men together and they hid in the forest that young Václav of Vrabinec was to pass through. He fell upon him and ordered him to be bound and thrown into Střekov jail.

"So you see," Kuba mocked his prisoner, "you were right that I ambush people, but being right will not bring you much joy."

He had the young knight of Vrabinec taken to a cell in the Střekov cliff, and he and his men went on to Vrabinec castle. The lord of Vrabinec, the prisoner's father, defended himself with a handful of brave men. But what could the castle garrison do against greater numbers? Kuba's band climbed over the ramparts and Kuba himself struck the old man's sword from his hand and was about to deal the fatal blow.

At that moment it was as if a geyser of gold had gushed up between Kuba's sword and the old knight. The old man's fair-haired daughter had thrown herself between the sword and her father. Kuba saw her beauty and his sword dropped.

"Save my father!" she cried. "We shall reward you, only save my father's life!"

"I shall leave your father alone," said Kuba, though he still held the unsheathed sword in his hand. "I will save your father's life, so you should see I am not as bad as they say of me. I will even free from prison your brother, whom you think is coming home any minute. For all that I wish for no reward. But—you must become my wife."

The castle lord's beautiful daughter was struck dumb and could not take her eyes from the blade of Kuba's sword which, without striking, had severed her life. She had long ago chosen Sir Otto to be her husband, and she was to have become his wife as soon as Otto returned from abroad. And so on one side of the scales was her love for Otto, and on the other two lives, her father's and her brother's. She was afraid to look into Kuba's coarse face. She bowed her head and, still on her knees, she said:

"If you will grant mercy to my father and my brother, I will become your wife."

101

Kuba sheathed his sword and called to his men to stop their plundering. Then he invited the father and daughter to the castle hall, as if he were lord there, and ordered food and drink to be brought from the castle cellars. The intruder played host and celebrated the enforced engagement in wine that was not his own. Under the gaze of the golden-haired girl he even attempted better manners than were his wont. But do what you will, if a wolf were to pour a whole bin of flour into its pelt, it would still not become a lamb.

The strange feast ended and Sir Kuba took the castle lord's daughter off to Střekov, to his thieves' den on the cliff. He let Václav of Vrabinec out of the dungeon and jeered at him with the words: "Go your way, noble Sir, ornament of the knightly state. From today I am your brother-in-law, and I cannot allow my wife to have a brother in prison."

From his sister's face and from her tears Václav of Vrabinec read what had happened. He clenched his fists and would have hurled himself on Kuba with bare hands. But Kuba nodded and the guard seized the young knight, dragged him out of the castle entrance and locked the gates behind him. The waters of the Elbe beneath Střekov castle covered over with ice, the sheets of ice melted in the spring sun, summer passed and again yellow leaves floated on the river's surface.

Sir Kuba changed more quickly than the weather. At one moment he forced himself to courteousness, at the next he was seized with fury when he saw how his wife was suffering. He would ride out into the country for wild skirmishes and robbery, often only returning at night.

One night, when Sir Kuba was out somewhere and the autumn wind blustered round the Střekov towers and wailed, Kuba's unhappy wife was slumbering and she dreamt that the man she had once willingly chosen as her husband, Sir Otto, had come into the room.

"Otto," she spoke his name from her dream and her own voice woke her. She looked round the twilit room in confusion. The torch hanging on the wall was burning low, and something moved in the dark corner. There was a goblin in the corner, he was stroking his long silver beard, and when he spoke his voice was as thin as tinfoil.

"Don't be afraid of me," the goblin addressed the amazed young woman, "we goblins live in the Střekov cliff, and we know all the prisoners who have ever been in prison there. Now the man whom you just called is in prison there. Kuba attacked Sir Otto and imprisoned him. Tomorrow morning he will have him executed. If you want to save him, you must hurry. It will not be difficult— the guard has fallen asleep. But hurry."

The goblin disappeared, the torch spluttered and went out. Kuba's wife ran through the well-known passages to the prison. The guard was sleeping in front of the iron-studded door. The young woman managed to open the door and went down the steps. She took off Otto's fetters and led him out.

It was a sad meeting between the formerly engaged couple and a brief one. Shouting and noise proclaimed that Kuba was back from his foray. Sir Otto disappeared in the darkness and escaped from the castle.

At dawn shrieks and lamentation resounded through the Střekov courtyard. Sir Kuba was cruelly punishing the guard who had let the precious prisoner, Sir Otto, escape.

But then Kuba's wife came out of the castle and said:

"Do not punish him, but me, if you wish to magnify the punishment I endure by living with you. I let Sir Otto out of prison in the night. I am the guilty one."

Rage overcame Sir Kuba. He knocked his wife down to the ground and dragged her by her long golden hair high up onto the battlements. From there he hurled her into the depths below Střekov. As she fell the sharp cliffs wounded her, a hundred blows tore her body and she fell to the foot of the cliff dead. The Střekov goblins came out of their holes and hiding-places and buried her soulless body and they buried her golden hair. They sang at her grave with silver voices and all the waves of the Elbe sang with them.

It is said that on autumn nights Kuba's young wife climbs up the cliff to the place from where she was thrown, and her long white figure trembles in the wind. The hearts of those who see her vain attempts are gripped with anxiety.

Sir Otto then joined up with the young knight of Vrabinec and together they conquered Střekov and burnt it down, but they did not find Kuba amongst those they captured. He had escaped at the last moment. But nowhere did he find calm. All his crimes followed after him wherever he went. His wanderings took him as far as Jerusalem. And there the Saracens attacked him and treacherously took his life. So Sir Kuba travelled to a distant country for the same death he had prepared for others all through his life.

Náchod

NÁCHOD

THE KNIGHT OF NÁCHOD

It is said that long, long ago a knight lived in Náchod castle who wanted to become the ruler of the Czech Lands. he was powerful and rich, the lord of many people, but all that was too little for him.

If I had more gold and silver, he thought, I should surely be able to overthrow the Prague prince and then I should rule the whole country...

And he decided he would ask the old witch of the Náchod forest for advice.

For a long time the witch warned the knight. But in the end she was persuaded and told him how to lay his hands on gold. He was to pluck a flower of the golden fern before St. John's Day, and with this flower go round the cliff beside Náchod castle. From that cliff gushed a golden spring and only he might draw from it who held the golden fern.

The knight listened eagerly.

Yes, he would take the gold from the spring in a jug and pour it out in front of the cliff. then the gold would be his, and when it hardened on the ground he would be able to carry it away.

The witch warned the lord of Náchod that he must be sure not to lose the flower of the golden fern. Otherwise the elves who were masters of the golden spring would revenge themselves on him.

The knight ran to seek the golden fern. He found it, for it shone on the slopes like a flame. He plucked a flower and hastened to the cliff. It opened beneath the touch of the fern as if he had unlocked it with a key. He took gold from the dazzling spring, poured it out in front of the cliff, and ran into the cliff again.

He gazed bemused at the flowing gold. What did he care for the elves, who were watching him intently. After all, he had the magic flower.

But he was not careful enough. When he was bailing up the gold he dropped the fern into the spring...

The magic cliff closed and the knight disappeared for ever. And so the lord of Náchod did not become the ruler of the Czech Lands.

ZVÍKOV

THE DAUGHTER OF FOREFATHER ČECH

The place where the ancient castle of Zvíkov stands has tempted people to settle there since time immemorial.

And it is said that this delightful place became the home of the oldest daughter of the man who brought the tribe of the Czechs to their new homeland, Forefather Čech.

The Forefather's daughter knew that her father would never consent to her marrying the man she loved, but she took him as her husband even against her father's will. And then she decided: the only way open to her and her man was to escape from her father's anger to a place beyond the reach of his power.

In those days southern Bohemia was wild and uninhabited country. And the young couple became lost, as it seemed for ever, in the depths of the south Bohemian forest.

Where Zvíkov castle stands today they built themselves a log cabin. They lived there alone, with no retinue, no servants, as the simplest of simple people. The man went out hunting and the woman cooked what he brought over the fire... They had no riches but those brought by their happy hearts. But both the man and the woman knew that there was no greater gift on this earth.

And it happened that one day the Forefather of the tribe of the Czechs came to wild southern Bohemia. He walked through the almost impenetrable forest with his company. And suddenly he saw some children playing on a woodland cliff.

He was astonished.

What were children doing in this deserted place?

He called them to him. The children greeted the old man politely. And when he asked them to show him

Zvíkov

where they lived, one of the children took him by the hand and led him home...

A beautiful girl was standing in front of the hut. She was gazing into the distance, and there were tears in her eyes. She was remembering...

Then she saw the children and her father.

She ran to meet them. And father and daughter fell into each other's arms. The Forefather had long ago forgiven his daughter, and his anger at her decision had been replaced by an immense melancholy.

When his daughter's husband came back from the hunt there was a complete reconciliation. But the Forefather tried in vain to persuade his daughter to bring her family back to their old settlement by Říp Hill. She had grown to love the country there and had found her home in it. And it is said that in the end her father agreed and told his company to build his daughter a fine seat there, instead of the poor shack. And because his daughter had grown accustomed to that place, they called the seat Zvykov (zvyk = custom in Czech. Translator's note). And today this beautiful place is named Zvíkov.

Jindřichův Hradec

JINDŘICHŮV HRADEC
ČESKÝ KRUMLOV

ON LADIES OF THE CASTLE

In the ancient days of our country a mighty lord of many estates and castles lived in southern Bohemia. His name was Vítek. He had five sons and at the close of his life he gave each of them property and to each he bequeathed the emblem of his family—a rose of five petals.

To his oldest son, Jindřich or Henry, Lord Vítek left a blue shield with a golden rose, and of his castles he gave him Hradec. To his son Vilém he entrusted a silver rose on a red shield and he gave him Třeboň. Vítek's son Smil received a blue rose on a golden shield and the Stráž estates. Vok got a red rose on a white shield from his father and the Rožmberk and Krumlov estates. And Sezima, according to his father's wishes, took a white shield with a black rose and obtained Ústí.

Then the whole tribe was called after their ancestor Vítek, the Vítkovice tribe. After their emblem they were called the Lords of the Rose. And just as roses fade and die, and new buds sprout on the rose twigs, so one family of the Vítkovice died and became extinct, and others flourished. But like the scent of rose bushes from distant gardens, there reaches us from remote ages the renown for goodness of the women who lived in the castles belonging to the Lords of the Rose.

The first of them was named Markéta and she was the wife of Jindřich, Lord of Hradec. Lady Markéta was gracious and kind to their subjects and won their favour through her generosity. She well knew that an outstretched palm can do more with poor underlings than fingers clenched in a fist that threatens. Once Lord Jindřich was rebuilding his castle and he wanted it finished before the frosts set in. Lady Markéta went amongst the workmen, encouraged them and made promises.

"Work hard, good people, work hard," she would say. "When you finish building the castle the lord will give you cake and I will cook some sweet pap for you. And in memory of the good work we shall meet here year after year. As long as this castle stands I shall invite you and your children to a feast."

The workmen worked hard and honestly and they finished the castle before ice covered the river. And in the castle kitchen cakes were baked and sweet pap cooked. In the courtyard tables and benches were screwed together, and everyone who had worked sat down to the feast. Jugs of beer went the rounds from mouth to mouth, and plates of cake, fish and pap covered the table tops, and delicious sweet steam rose from the pap. In the middle of this great feasting the sky suddenly became overcast and the first snowflakes fell to the ground. Then they whirled in the air and winter began to spread a white cloth for its feast.

Lady Markéta was upset that the snow had spoiled her feast.

From then on she cooked the sweet pap in the spring, when the snow had thawed. At Eastertide, on Maundy Thursday every year the bell in the old tower called all the poor bondsmen together for a feast. And it is said that there used to be several thousand of them.

In Telč too, which belonged to the lords of Hradec, the custom was kept up of inviting the poor to a feast once a year. That day became the festival of all poor wretches who never ate their fill the whole year through.

But sadness and care visit even the good and the kind. Lady Markéta's husband died. So she gave the estate over to her son and entered a nunnery. The people of Hradec only saw her now and then. She would come to visit her son in the white robe of her order.

When she died she entered legend in a white robe too. She would appear to people and, as when she was alive, so even after death she saw to it that the poor should receive every year what she had promised them.

Often her white robe would shine in the night in the dark castle halls. She walked through them like a good guardian who is awake when the castle servants sleep. She wandered through the passages that she had known so well in her lifetime, she went out into the courtyard and onto the ramparts, and her soundless steps were accompanied by a slight clinking of the bunch of keys tied to her waist.

Once it is said that people saw her at high noon at a window in the tower. She was hovering there like white steam, and when the people down below greeted her respectfully, she greeted them too with a nod and a smile. Then she vanished into thin air.

Other castles of Lords of the Rose were visited by a white lady too. The best known of them was Lady Perchta of Rožmberk. When she was young they married her to a noble lord who was both rich and powerful. But he lacked a good heart. The young wife suffered in the foreign surroundings at his side, and only her husband's death freed her from being slighted and humiliated. She came back with her spirit refined by suffering and became the benefactress of those in need and distress. She understood their misery, pain and hardship, and never deserted them in their trouble. Even after her death she remained at Krumlov castle as a slender figure of light.

She took care too of the last offspring of the Lords of Rožmberk. That was the famous Petr Vok of Rožmberk. At night when the nurses were asleep, she would take the child in her arms and soothe its crying. Once it happened that the nurse surprised her doing this and shouted at her:

"Leave that child alone! Mind your own affairs!"

"The child is more mine than yours," the white lady answered and raised her hand against the wall. The wall swallowed her and the terrified nurse realized whom she had seen.

When Lord Petr Vok was grown up, the nurse told him of that strange event. Lord Petr ordered that the

Český Krumlov

wall should be dug up at that place and he found a great treasure hidden in it.

Pictures of women long since dead survived for many centuries in the likenesses of white ladies who, even after they were dead, could not forego good deeds, care and solicitude. The quiet clinking of keys announces their arrival. They unlock legends and enter into them. They are always on the side of good people, and anyone who has pure thoughts need not be afraid of them.

Hluboká

HLUBOKÁ

ZÁVIŠ OF FALKENŠTEJN

Lord Záviš of Falkenštejn...

He was one of the most romantic figures during the reign of the last of the Přemyslides. A rich magnate who became the favourite of Queen Kunhuta, widowed mother of King Wenceslas II.

As long as Queen Kunhuta lived, Záviš's power remained uncontested. He placed his friends in important places at the Prague court, he had great influence over the young ruler and he seemed invulnerable. But every summit looks down into an abyss. Queen Kunhuta died and Záviš's power lost its certainty. His enemies, both overt and secret, multiplied. And the prince became King Wenceslas II.

Once again it seemed that happiness had turned its face to Záviš. He made a bid for the hand of the Hungarian king's sister Elizabeth. At that time Elizabeth lived in a convent and the Pope delayed giving his permission to the marriage. But then the fierce and violent Hungarian king had his soldiers drive off the monks who guarded Elizabeth, and took his sister to live with him. Then a festive wedding was celebrated between Záviš of Falkenštejn and Elizabeth.

After the wedding Záviš took his new wife to the great castle of Svojanov, where he saw to her comfort. While he was engaged in Svojanov castle with matters far removed from court affairs, his enemies were gaining the upper hand at the royal court.

At Svojanov Elizabeth of Hungary gave birth to a son, and his christening was to be a great ceremony. The Hungarian king had promised to come to Svojanov, and the Bohemian King Wenceslas II. had been invited too. Svojanov castle was bustling with activity, and Záviš of

Falkenštejn rode out with his company to Prague, to give the Bohemian king a worthy escort.

For a long time Wenceslas II. had not trusted Záviš, his former advisor and administrator. Those who opposed Záviš had slowly but surely come to dominate Prague Castle. From all sides alarming reports reached the king.

Záviš is planning your ruin, my king! He is conspiring with the Hungarian king to take your life. The christening feast at Svojanov is to be your last feast. The magic is prepared, the poison mixed, the knives sharpened.

Záviš had as many enemies as he once had friends. The Bohemian king's ears had not changed, but his surroundings had. One of Záviš's enemies was Guta, Wenceslas's wife, who was a Habsburg. She feared Záviš and shared distrust of him with her father.

Lord Záviš entered under the roof of Prague Castle as an unsuspecting fish swims into a net. He brought Queen Guta a valuable veil, but it was said all over Prague that the queen never even touched the veil. What if a magic spell had been woven into the veil, the evil force of which would overpower the queen? Hardly had lord Záviš left the hall than she told her servants to burn the precious veil.

When lord Záviš wanted to leave the castle palace, nine knights stepped in his path. Nine swords challenged his single sword. He kept up his defense for a long time, but he could not win. He was captured and bound and thrown into the White Tower of Prague castle.

Wenceslas kept Záviš prisoner for two years, and tried to force him to give up his castles. For two years Záviš refused, and his castles remained loyal to him. At last the Bohemian king, on the advice of his friends, ordered that Záviš be taken all over Bohemia, to all his castles, one after another. The castle garrisons saw from the ramparts their lord Záviš standing in chains with an executioner behind him.

"Surrender," the besiegers called up to the castle. "Surrender, or the executioner will perform his duty on your lord."

The people in the castle were horrified, but Záviš stood firm, showing no emotion.

Some castles surrendered under this threat. The royal army then advanced to the next castle. The army with its precious captive came in time to Hluboká castle. There the burgrave was Záviš's brother Vítek.

The royal forces put on their usual show with the executioner below Hluboká castle. The burgrave Vítek saw and heard them, but he ignored them. He thought it all a cunning trick and empty drum-beating.

The commander of the royal army, Mikuláš of Opava, was one of Záviš of Falkenštejn's main enemies. He had the king's confidence and was permitted to deal with the prisoner as he thought fit. The defiance shown by Záviš's brother increased Mikuláš's hatred. He waited and waited till the castle gates should at last be opened. And then he lost patience. He ordered a scaffold to be set up. The people from the castle watched the preparations and did not believe their eyes. Mikuláš commanded the executioner to do his duty. The people from the castle saw lord Záviš kneel before the executioner. Still they did not believe. Then the executioner cut off Záviš's head with a sharp piece of wood.

Under the blue August sky the head of Záviš of Falkenštejn fell and blood dyed the grass. And it is said that the place spattered with blood bore red grass for many years.

Legend says that the Bohemian king's mind was not at peace, and he began all the more to seek the peace and calm that he could not find amongst people in the service of the Christian God.

Orlík

ORLÍK

THE EAGLE'S NEST

It is told that once there lived in the Orlice woods a band of merciless robbers, led by the famous robber Batěk.

Often the army tried to catch the robbers and destroy them. But it seemed that the robbers were invulnerable. The deep woods that they knew so well were excellent cover for them.

The robbers lived in the woods with their wives and children, they felt quite safe, and were as used to life in the woods as other people are used to life in towns.

But it happened that the contentment of the leader of the robber band, Batěk, soon came to an end. His beautiful young wife fell ill and died. Only his little son was left to the robber chief, just a child and a great grief.

Batěk, who had killed so many people, started to fear death. He was not afraid for his own life, but was terrified that death might take away the child he loved... He had the child carefully guarded, he told all the robbers to keep an eye on it... He was desperate over the death of his wife and desperate over the danger that might be awaiting his child.

In vain they tried to comfort him, that all of them were watching over the safety of his child.

One day Batěk came back to the robbers' camp from a foray and the nurse told him in tears that his son had disappeared.

Where? How could he disappear, when no one had come into the camp?

The robbers searched every bush, every bank and ravine. But Batěk's child was nowhere to be found. They walked through the woods and called, Batěk raced through those woods like a madman, calling the boy's name again and again.

At dawn next day they set out to search for the child again. One of the robbers decided to climb up to the highest cliff and look around from there, whether he could not see a trace of him somewhere.

When he had scrambled up to the very top of the rocky cliff he saw an eagle's nest. Lying in it, amongst the eaglets, was the robber chief's little son, sleeping happily, snuggled up to the birds of prey. The robber dragged him out of the nest and carefully climbed down the cliff.

No one could have tied the child to his chest, found him, or imagined where he had got to—the eagle had grabbed him, carried him up high and flown with him to its nest.

Robber Batěk was changed by the anxiety he had suffered, fear for his child had marked him. He realized what anxiety the relatives of those he had attacked must have experienced for their dear ones, thanks to him. He gave up robbery and built a strong castle on the cliff where the eagle's nest had been, and to this day the castle bears the beautiful and proud name Orlík—the Eagle.

RADYNĚ
KAŠPERK

FROM THE STORIES OF IMPERIAL CASTLES

The deeds of King Charles were many, and many of them left their mark on the face of our country. Charles's works and deeds were the fulfilment of the dreams and efforts of his predecessors. He gave Prague a university, which Wenceslas II. had already striven for, he gave her a new stone bridge, magnificent churches and he built the New Town of Prague. But we shall now leave Prague behind and enter thick forests where the axes of woodcutters can be heard on the hills, and in the clearings castles are being built to strengthen and protect the king, his country and his treasures.

The king in his time founded many castles and he liked to give them his name. In those days there grew up near Plzeň Karlskrone castle, Charles's crown, in the Šumava mountains Karlsberg, Charles's hill.

Karlskrone castle did not bear that name for long, people started to call it Radyně. Legend tells that an immense treasure of gold and silver and precious stones glitters and glows in the underground vaulted halls there. Among the heaps of gems stands an iron chest and on the chest slumbers a great black dog. Or is he slumbering? If anyone entered the cellar he would hurl himself upon them. These treasures are said to have been hidden in the underground halls by the knight Sir Raden. He was mighty and he was rich, but he was unhappy. The shape of his ears was not human. They were like bat's wings. And Raden longed, if he could not rid himself of his ears, at least for his successors not to have such a heritage from him. But whenever a child was born to his wife, it was born with inhuman ears. In desperation Raden killed all his children. His misery and despondency did not leave

124

him even after death. He found no calm in the grave and walks his old castle—a sad, restless ghost.

It is related that there was then no lack of gold in Bohemia, especially in the south, where the Šumava mountains closed the ring of mountains embracing the Czech Lands. It is said that gold was found here in great quantities and of rare purity. One day the gold-diggers of the Šumava golden mountains found a boulder of gold and, after consulting together, they sent it to the Emperor Charles. And the emperor longed to see with his own eyes the place that yielded such excellent and precious metal. He set out with his company to the Šumava mountains, sought out the gold-diggers' camp, received their leader and listened to him.

A lighted lamp lures moths in the night, the glitter of gold lured thieves. They would come out at opportune moments from the thick forests, attack the gold-diggers and take away their gold.

"Help us, Your Imperial Majesty, from the bands of thieves," the gold-diggers begged the Emperor Charles.

Even the devil, as ancient legends state, scented gold from afar and ran up to confuse the heads of those who brought up gold from the earth.

"Help us, Your Imperial Majesty, from the devils. On windy nights their hoofs scurry over our work and trample it down and they pour water into our pits. Their invisible fur is wiped over our bread and spoils our food and brings sickness."

The emperor pondered and after a moment's thought he said:

"This region lacks a castle. A castle means order and protection and the bell of the castle chapel will frighten away all impure forces."

At these words he ordered the horses to be saddled and he rode into the woods with his company to seek for a place to build a castle. The surrounding country was wild, the narrow paths were overgrown with thickets, the horses had to step or jump over tree-trunks felled by age or tempests. Elsewhere boulders lay in the way, as if the devil had laid them in the emperor's path. Legend tells that in the tangle of branches, tree-trunks and stones the emperor lost his company. He pushed aside the thick wall of a hazel grove and stood on the edge of a wide clearing. A mountain stream sang at his feet and beyond the clearing, above the tree-tops of young fir-trees, a peak towered to the blue sky. The emperor tied his horse to the stump of a tree, stepped over the stream and made across the clearing. The peak that rose over the wood seemed to have been made for a castle to be built on it. Deep in thought the emperor came to the far side of the clearing. Suddenly he was torn from his thoughts by the sound of shouting. He looked round and noticed a poor hut, such as charcoal-burners build in the woods. In front of the hut an old man was jumping about, brandishing a stick, beating the air, thrashing around himself, shouting, but no enemy was to be seen.

The emperor came nearer.

"Hey, charcoal-burner," he called to the old man, "what is it you are doing?"

The charcoal-burner stopped waving his stick for a moment, but he still held his left hand in front of him clenched into a fist, as if he were holding something.

"Noble Sir," said the charcoal-burner, who did not know whom he was speaking to, "I am struggling with the devil. I have to fight him every day. He minds my felling trees here, burning coal, he minds my working here. Today I have given it him thick and fast. He pretends he can't go on and thinks I'll let him go. But I've got him by the tail, and I shan't let go. I'll go on beating him." And the charcoal-burner raised his gnarled stick and again started to strike the invisible devil.

Then a tremendous peal of thunder reverberated and with it the daylight was extinguished. Darkness fell on the emperor and the old man, who started again to wield his stick and shout. The darkness was riven by violet streaks of lightning and in their light the emperor groped his way to the hut. Just in time. Hardly had he got under the roof than a downpour pelted down outside and a blustering

Kašperk

wind roared in the tree-tops and howled and wailed. It seemed as if all of hell was hurrying to the aid of the struggling devil.

Suddenly, as if you would run out of a cellar, there was daylight again everywhere and the blue sky gazed down on up-rooted trees, broken branches and grass covered with mud and sand.

The emperor came out of the hut. A few steps away lay the old man, lifeless, struck by lightning, the stick fallen from his rigid fingers.

The emperor thought for a long time about the dead charcoal-burner, about good that must be cultivated like a peerless flower, and about evil that multiplies itself like weeds. Slowly he returned to the place where he had tethered his horse on the edge of the wood. And then he heard hunting-horns. The imperial company rode out into the clearing.

"Listen well," said the emperor to his knights, "I will tell you what happened to me." And he told them about the charcoal-burner and the devil and the storm. Then he pointed to the peak that rose above the forest and he said: "There we will build a castle to thwart all the forces of evil that impede hard-working people in their work."

A castle was built on the peak and it was given the name Karlsberg or Kašperk. But the devils in the region did not give up. Perhaps that was why so many knights alternated in holding the new castle. But nor did the emperor give up his fight against evil.

PŘIMDA

A MYSTERIOUS CASTLE

One day Prince Oldřich was following a doe and he became separated from his fellows except for one young man, eager but inexperienced. They lost the doe in the green half-light of the forest and when they were returning round a marsh suddenly a magnificent wild boar charged at them. The youth stood stock-still with fear and did not even manage to raise his crossbow. Oldřich reached for his spear, but the boar was quicker. He hurled himself upon the horses. At that moment a spear flew out of the thicket, hitting the boar so mightily that it pierced his throat and nailed him to the root of a tree. A young man stepped out of the thicket and if Oldřich had not been a Christian he would have taken him for a sylvan god, hastening to the aid of the unlucky huntsman.

"Who are you?" the prince asked the strange young man.

"They call me Koc," said the man, "I help in the mill beyond the wood."

"You saved our horses, and who knows if you didn't save our lives. You are brave, you have a steady hand and a good eye. I need such men as you in my retinue. Come with me, you will get a horse, a suit of clothes and a weapon. I am Prince Oldřich. Whoever is in my company lacks for nothing."

The young man bowed deeply to the prince and took his offer as a distinction and a blessing.

Later the prince bestowed on him the part of the country in which this incident happened. Koc built a castle there on a nearby hill and gave it the name Dobrš. Thus he became the founder of the family of Koc of Dobrš. The lords of Dobrš then always had a millwheel in their coat-of-arms, in memory of their ancestor who had once worked in a mill.

Prince Oldřich proceeded with his train of huntsmen through the frontier Šumava forest, enjoying hunting in a country so rich in game. He was a tireless huntsman and it would happen that the company sat down to rest, but the prince did not leave the saddle. He rode out to survey the surroundings and only came back when the fire was lit.

On one such survey he rode out of the wood onto an open glade and when he raised his head he saw a hill above the tree-tops and on it a castle. He did not tarry to call the company, but turned his horse up the hill to the castle.

It was a strange castle. Everywhere it was empty and lifeless, only bushes and trees had attacked the ramparts and earthworks and their branches moved in the light evening breeze. The castle gateway was wide open and there was no bridge across the moat—it had rotted and fallen to the moat's bottom. The prince tied up his horse and crossed the moat by way of an uprooted fir tree. The courtyard was overgrown with grass and there was no sign of life anywhere. The prince entered the castle palace. He saw a table still littered with plates, a bit of clothing on a chair and in the cold fireplace a cauldron with mouldering remains of food in it. He saw a chamber filled with supplies, wormy flour, stone-hard bread, sacks and baskets covered with mildew. In another chamber was a chest with the mouldering robes of a noble lady, a nobleman's array falling apart, moulting furs. All these clothes were outmoded in cut and fashion. Lastly Prince Oldřich went down to the cellars and groping found some barrels. He knocked on them and recognized that they were full. He tasted the contents of the nearest and there was the sweet flavour of excellent old wine on his tongue.

Meanwhile darkness had fallen. He had to get back to his company. Oldřich mounted the overgrown ramparts and saw a reddish light below him in the forest. His huntsmen had lit a fire there. The prince crossed the moat over the tree-trunk, untied his horse and set out in the direction of the fire. But the strange deserted castle gave him no peace. Its mystery irked him like a quarry that escaped him.

He sat down by the fire and told of what he had seen. None of his men had any idea that a castle towered on a hill near their camp. And no one knew that any castle had ever stood in those parts.

Over the following days the prince ceased his favourite pastime of hunting and searched whether he could not find out who had been the lord of the unknown castle and why he had deserted it and left his entire property within its walls.

After lengthy inquiries he found an old man in a lonely place who knew the story of the castle from his father, and his father knew it again from his father. And this was the story:

Once a young man of noble birth had lived at the court of the German emperor. He had come to the court to learn court manners, as befitted a knight. The young man was well-built, handsome of face and quick to learn. He was competent in bearing and in speech.

The German emperor of that time had a lovely daughter. The young nobleman and the emperor's daughter would meet, and whenever they met they would drop their eyes in sudden embarrassment. But the love that troubled them secretly made them turn to look at each other and to seek out places where they could meet. Whether it was in church, in the garden or at a ball in the castle halls, wherever one of them was, the other was sure to be near. And in time their love grew and ceased to drop its eyes. One day they talked together, the next day they embraced, and the third day they kissed. They promised themselves to one another and swore that they would never part. Their love was a delight to them, yet filled them with fear. There was no hope that they could marry. The emperor would never allow his daughter to become the wife of a nobleman's son. He wanted to marry her to a man of royal family.

The young noble was tormented and thought for days and nights how to fulfil their wish. In the end he invented a plan, and when he had invented it he began to carry it out. He sold his estates and left the service of the court. Then he bade a secret farewell to the emperor's daughter and promised her that he would return when a lucky star appeared in the heavens. He went from the emperor's castle straight into the forest. He rode in deeper and deeper, along paths where the horse could scarcely pass, searching in the depths of the forest for a suitable place. It was to be hidden from human sight, with no village far and wide, not even a solitary house nor a fort, but from it there was to be a view on all sides.

For long he rode, paths or no paths, till he stood on a hill in the forest on the Czech side of the frontier. The place on the hill was remote, hidden, far from human dwellings, and yet there was a view far over the country.

The young nobleman brought workmen there, to the top of the hill, and told them to start building. A castle began to grow on the hill in the midst of those wooded slopes. The noble urged the workmen to hasten, as though he were expecting an enemy on the morrow. The emperor's daughter used to stand in the courtyard of the imperial castle every evening, gazing at the heavens and watching for her lucky star.

The castle in the frontier woods was finished. The noble led the workmen into a hut and ordered that wine be poured for them. The workmen drank and those who poured for them drank too. When they were all drunk and had fallen asleep the noble, the only sober man among them, went out, locked the door behind him and set fire to the hut. Thus he rid himself of inconvenient witnesses to the building and by that cruel deed erased all traces that were left.

In the misty dawn he set out on horseback for the imperial castle. He only reached it in the evening, when the stars came out. Today there was a lucky star among them and under its light he entered the courtyard. He told the emperor's daughter that he had had a castle built for her and supplies of food brought, so that they could hide there till the emperor's anger passed. That very night the emperor's daughter left her father's castle with the young nobleman. On the way they were secretly married in a village church and then the green surface of the forest closed over them.

For five years the emperor knew nothing of them, nor did the world. In the fifth year the emperor was staying in the town of Regensburg, and from there he rode out to hunt in the forests between Bavaria and Bohemia. Once in the heat of the hunt he crossed onto the territory of Bohemia. Suddenly the emperor found himself alone with his horse in the midst of a darkening wood, surrounded by the branches of trees. He blew his horn as a sign to his company, but no one answered. Again he blew his hunting horn, but echo gave him back only the sound of his own horn. So the emperor decided to find his way himself. In those days the Bohemian forests were thick and far-reaching, and anyone lost in them could hardly find the way back. The emperor completely lost his bearings and wandered for three days and three nights, eating only forest fruits and drinking from the forest wells. At dawn on the third day he saw a castle tower in front of him on a wooded hill. The emperor rejoiced and spurred on his horse. Light but persistent rain had been falling since midnight and the emperor's clothes were soaked, he looked forward to warming himself at a glowing hearth.

He approached the castle gateway and blew his horn. The gate opened and the emperor stood face to face with his son-in-law whom he did not recognise. The young couple had been hidden for so long that they thought they were already forgotten. They were eager for any news of the world, and therefore from time to time they allowed unknown travellers into their castle. So they gave the emperor food and drink and dried his clothes for him. After the meal they asked him about this and that. The emperor soon realized whom he was speaking to, but they did not recognize him.

"And how is the emperor, what news of him?" asked his daughter.

"Have you not heard that the emperor is no longer alive?" the emperor pretended to be surprised and told them an invented story about the emperor's death and burial.

"Ah, the poor emperor," wailed the emperor's daughter, "but perhaps quiet will reign now and my husband will no longer have to fear any evil."

The emperor slept in the castle and the next day asked the way to Regensburg and departed. But not for long. He summoned princes, had their armies summoned, and with a mighty throng of armed men he advanced to beneath the castle of his undesired son-in-law. He surrounded the castle and sent a messenger to his son-in-law with the message:

"I have eaten your bread, I have drunk your wine, I have slept under your roof. But you carried off my daughter and violated my imperial will, and therefore I too shall do violence to you."

This bode the nobleman ill. He had no army, nor had he even a weapon that he could use against so numerous an enemy. The bowstrings of the catapults had long ago rotted, the swords were gnawed by rust. He looked down from the battlements and saw an army preparing to attack. The emperor's daughter saw her husband was suffering, and she heard the commands below the castle. She went out on the rampart and called to the advancing soldiers:

"Advance boldly, press forward, a thousand soldiers against a single man. But bear in mind that if you take my husband's life neither shall I want to live. I shall hurl myself from the rampart and so end my own life."

When the emperor heard this he commanded the attack to be stopped and consulted with the princes. On their advice and that of his own heart, he changed his mind. He granted his daughter's husband mercy. The nobleman and the emperor's daughter came out of the castle, knelt before the emperor and he received them both as his children. Then they hurriedly left the region that reminded them of the harrowing moments of the last day.

It is said that Prince Oldřich gave the deserted castle

to a member of his company who was named Prím. In this castle he was to stand on guard at the frontier of the Czech land. And legend tells that Prím gave the castle the name Přimda.

BEZDĚZ

A MAGICAL GOBLET

Legend tells us that Czech lords added their number to those knights who were heading for the south, to the Holy Land. They left their castles and their families, sword in hand, and made their way towards the heart of the heathen country. Not all of them returned. And those who did return had usually left their health in the hot territories of Africa and Asia around the Mediterranean. They came home only to lay their bones in the soil of their native land.

And more and more knights joined the new crusades against the heathen. Some out of Christian conviction, some out of longing for adventure, and others out of greed for gold and precious stones. The castle lord went from Bezděz too, and left his wife and children. His wife was a good lady, kind and knowing of healing and medicinal herbs. People would come to her with their illnesses from all over the country, and she was able to advise them all and give remedies.

Only she knew no remedy for her loneliness. She thought of her far-away husband and would have given a fortune to know that he would return to her from the crusades alive and well. Worry about him kept her awake at night. She lay staring into the dark and waited for sleep to take her from her sad thoughts.

One night she was again lying on her bed, not sleeping and thinking, when she heard a quiet creaking in the darkness, as if someone was carefully opening the door. A little blue light crept into the bedroom through a crack in the half-open doorway, it glimmered low on the floor, and when the lady looked closely at that place, she saw that the light came from a tiny lantern held by an elf with a long white beard.

"Lady…" whispered the elf.

Bezděz

But the lady was silent, she could not make a sound for surprise. And the elf called her again and yet again.

The lady plucked up courage, sat up in bed and asked:

"Who are you and what do you want?"

"My lady," said the elf, "our king's daughter is sick, and if you do not help her, no one will. Come with me and bring your herbs, ointments and medicines. Help her. We shall never forget it."

As soon as the lady heard that the elf was asking for her help she got up, dressed quickly, took her medicines and hurried after the blue light that flickered before her near the ground.

They went out of the bedroom, and when they had only taken a few steps along the castle passage the elf stopped in front of the wall. He lifted the little lantern and there in the blue light was a small door that had never been there before. The elf opened the door and led the lady down stairs, deeper and deeper into the heart of the hill on which the castle stood. The further they descended the more the light increased.

"Here we are," said the elf, and around them it was broad daylight.

In the midst of a meadow that sparkled as if it was made of glass and precious stones, stood a castle, but so small that the lady could not enter it. But a procession of elves came out of the castle, bearing the sick princess on a stretcher. The lady wasted no time looking about and did not hesitate. She examined the sick girl, poured some medicine for her into a crystal goblet, tipped out some spices, gave advice on how they should be boiled and when they should be given, and then let herself be led back the same way into her bedroom. Day was dawning outside the window when she lay down. In the morning the lady of the castle thought it had all been a dream. But when night came and again she could not sleep for worrying about her husband, the blue light appeared again. The elf bowed to the ground before her and said:

"Good my lady, the princess feels better after your medicine. The king of the elves sends you many thanks and this goblet full of happiness. Take care only not to break the goblet."

The elf had said his say, and the lady was overcome with a great tiredness, she closed her eyes and fell asleep, and slept until the sun woke her. Again she thought it had all been a dream. But on the ground by her bed stood the crystal goblet, shining in the morning sun. She saw at once that it was the goblet the elves had given her for the princess's medicine. She lifted it from the ground and as soon as she held it in her hands calling and trumpeting sounded from outside. The lord of the castle had returned safe and sound from the crusade. The lady put the goblet down carefully and hurried to meet her husband.

The goblet was held in great respect by the whole family and nobody dared drink from it, so that it should not be broken and with it the happiness that from that moment on did not desert the castle.

Years passed and the castle changed owners. The new knight found the goblet in the castle and listened to its story.

"Fairytales," he laughed, and he invited his noble friends from far and wide to a great banquet. In the middle of the feasting he ordered the crystal goblet to be brought and filled with wine. He raised the goblet on high, mockingly toasted all the elves in the country and shattered the goblet.

That same night one of his guests carried of his young daughter. The infuriated father leapt on his horse and set out after the abductor. But the wine he had drunk confused his senses and the paths. He hurtled from his horse and broke his neck. Not long after the knight's death Bezděz castle was burnt to the ground. Thus happiness was shattered together with the goblet.

KAMÝK
BLATNÁ

THE KNIGTHS TEMPLARS IN BOHEMIA

At the time of the crusades the order of the Knights Templars was established. King Baldwin then gave them part of the palace in Jerusalem where Soloman's temple used to stand. So they were given their name from the Latin word templum.

Legend tells that there was once a Templar's castle in Žernoseky. The knight who administered it was of a rough and violent nature. In those days there lived at Kamýk castle, to the west of Litoměřice, a castle lord and his blossoming daughter. His wife had died years ago and his daughter was his only joy and love and pride. And it was said that just as the lord of Kamýk was gentle and kindly, so was his daughter beautiful. Her long black locks were like a fragrant summer night and her face a clear, rosy star that had risen in that night.

Knights from all over Bohemia rode to Kamýk to look at her and to see if she would not like them. Many a helmet flashed in the castle courtyard, many a bright plume fluttered there and brave swords rang. All of them came in vain. And the pathway to the castle was so trampled by horses's hoofs that not a blade of grass grew on it.

One day the Knight Templar of Žernoseky appeared among the suitors. He approached the castle lord's daughter purposefully and abruptly. He wanted to see with his own eyes the girl who was called the rose of Kamýk. And as soon as he saw her he wanted to take her away with him. But the Templar's soldierly manner and violence had frightened the rose of Kamýk so much that she fled from him. So he returned home, but revenge flared in him like a tall and wicked fire.

On one day he thought up plans, the next day he put them into practice. He sent his armed men into

Kamýk

the thickets around Kamýk castle, told them where they should hide and at what time the castle lord's daughter went out for a walk with her ladies.

The rose of Kamýk left the castle at a certain hour, as was her custom. At that moment the woodland thickets were set in motion, the forest rustled and wailed, as if a wind had entered the branches. The armed men scattered the ladies, siezed the castle lord's daughter, and before the castle guard could reach the scene of the attack, the earth had swallowed the attackers.

Sorrow filled all the castle halls. The distraught lord sent messengers and searchers in every direction, but no one knew anything of the girl. In the end the knight, in desperation, disguised himself as a wandering troubadour and set out himself to visit castles and seek his lost child.

He came to know many castles, he heard many stories and reports from the castle servants, yet none of them concerned his daughter. How many times did he listen beneath gaol windows, how many times press his ear to the walls of castle prisons, but no prisoner's voice resembled the voice of his daughter.

He came on his wanderings to the Templar's castle in Žernoseky. No one recognised the lord of Kamýk in the wandering troubadour. Towards evening he found his way to the castle chapel. As he knelt there clasping his hands he suddenly heard weeping. Under the stone on which his tired, unflagging legs rested someone was lamenting and calling for help. The knight bent down to the stone and recognised his daughter's voice. It came from the dungeon beneath the chapel.

His heart wrung with pain, the knight speedily left Žernoseky and hurried to his castle. There in Kamýk he laid aside his troubadour clothes and donned armour. Then he called all who could bear arms and launched an attack on the Templars' castle. Anger and wrong sharpened his sword and longing for his daughter drove him on. Before the Templars could recover their senses the castle was conquered, the knight of Kamýk ran to the chapel with his most faithful band, ordered the stone to be lifted

142

and descended, torch in hand, to the dungeon. There lay his rose, lifeless. Death had freed her from suffering sooner than the lord of Kamýk could do so.

The knight of Kamýk came out of the dungeon pale and silent, bearing above his head the torch that had shone a moment earlier on his dead daughter. With that same torch he set fire to the castle, and whatever did not burn was rolled away and broken up by his people.

The story is told that the Bohemian castle of Blatná was also founded by the Templars. And that is because there used to be a very strange picture painted on the wall of the castle dining hall. In that picture Knights Templars were walking about a sad and rocky country. Some blackamoor was pointing out to them a boulder in front of him and shining a raised lantern on it.

One castle lord replaced another, but the picture remained in its place and no one knew what it represented. Until a young, inquisitive scribe came to the castle. During the day he pushed his quill over the castle documents, but at night he tossed uneasily and tried to solve the riddle of the picture. The Templars had a lot of gold, he said to himself, and he tried to find the connection between the Templars, the blackamoor and the place he was pointing to.

One night he was no longer able to contain his curiosity and his greed for gold. He crept out of his chamber on tip-toe and, by the light of his candle, began to examine the picture carefully, touching it and knocking on it. When he knocked on the place that the blackamoor was pointing to there was a hollow sound. The scribe did not stay to think long. That same night he ran to fetch a hammer and a piece of iron. He carefully peeled off the picture in that place, tapped cautiously with the hammer and levered with the iron. An opening came to light that led to a hiding-place full of gold and silver, rare jewels and precious vessels.

In the morning they searched for the scribe in vain. He escaped with his find, and since that day nobody has ever set eyes on him. All that remained after him was an opening in a picture painted on the wall. It is said that the damaged picture became dilapidated from that day and later fell to pieces altogether. It had fulfilled its purpose. It had given up the treasure and the treasure was the reason for its destruction.

A similar fate befell the leaders of the Order of Templars. When they were forced to surrender their property they ended in flames at the stake.

Valdštejn

VALDŠTEJN

THE VALDŠTEJN DRAGONS

Dragons, that's what the ordinary people used to call the vultures that had settled in the cliffs by the castle. They talk of them till this day. The enormous birds had never been seen in this part of the country, so they seemed to the people to be like dragons from fairytales. They did not eat only dead bodies, they hunted birds, rabbits and even dared to attack a young doe or a lamb. Indeed they were not afraid of humans, how many times had they soared up with a little child whose mother had not kept careful enough watch...

They had their nest on a cliff that was quite inaccessible. The castle lord of Valdštejn sent his soldiers to kill the vultures and rid the whole country from terror.

But the vultures appeared unexpectedly, they couldn't be caught. And while they were in their nest they were completely safe on that steep, smooth cliff...

People were afraid to leave their homes. And children were not allowed to take a step from the cottages...

At that time there was a prisoner in the Valdštejn dungeon. He had been condemned to death and was awaiting his end at the bottom of a deep hole.

It occurred to him that he might be able to save himself. He begged the castle lord to let him take up the struggle with the "dragons". If he conquered them he asked to be granted mercy...

The castle lord of Valdštejn agreed.

If he gave the prisoner his life he could save so many children.

The condemned man asked for a hammer and a chisel. He made some wooden pegs and fixed them into holes that he made in the vultures' cliff. And on them he slowly mounted the height towards the nest.

The exhausting work took him days, for days he climbed higher and higher, and those who watched him grew dizzy from the height he reached...

At last he climbed to the top of the cliff.

He used up the last peg.

People came from the whole region to see the fight. Even the lord of Valdštejn galloped up to the cliff, so as not to miss the prisoner's struggle.

The prisoner stood on the cliff, beside the nest.

The vultures fell on him... He fought them off with an axe, thrashing around himself, the vultures attacked from all sides with claws and beaks.

The prisoner overcame the "dragons".

And burnt their nest.

Then he climbed down and received mercy from the lord of Valdštejn.

From that day on the children have not had to be afraid to run out of the house into the garden...

KOST

AN INVINCIBLE CASTLE

In the region known as the Bohemian Paradise the mighty castle Kost* stands on a great cliff in the middle of a valley. Since ancient times it has had a name that recalls poverty and hunger, but the table in Kost castle used to be richly spread and groaned under the weight of food and drink. And where intemperance and luxury reigned no heart was ever to be found inclined to the belief of the Hussite priests. Their preaching spoke of abstemiousness and moderation and the simple way of life. The lords of great castles did not wish Žižka well.

The legend of Kost sees Žižka as he marches through the wooded valley below Kost castle, it hears the pounding of the mounted guards at the head of the army, the tramping of those on foot and the clatter of heavy carts as their wheels bump over the stones and potholes in the road. The Hussites stand below Kost and besiege it.

The warriors are armed with weapons that the castle garrison had never seen. The very weapons inspired fear. Iron-bound flails, sharp scythes, barbed globes chained to hafts—maces they were called—and hooks and cudgels spiked with pointed nails. Now, for fighting at a distance, cross-bows were pressed into use, huge siege slings, Hussite rifles and guns, from which Žižka's warriors shot great balls of stone.

But the castle resisted and did honour to its name. It was as hard as a bone. It is said that Žižka sat down to dinner many times at the stone table in the valley, many times he lay down to rest beneath the cliff, day followed night and night day, and victory receded.

After a number of days Žižka had to leave the valley, he could not afford a long siege. Duty called him elsewhere.

---

* "Kost" means "a bone" in Czech. Translator's note.

Kost

And it is said that on the way from Kost castle Žižka turned back to look at the mighty square tower and relieved his feelings with the words:

"A bone is for dogs!"

In later centuries, when the truth about Žižka's campaigns became mixed with inventions and stories, it was said of every castle that stood intact that Žižka had conquered it, though he had not conquered it, and of every castle that lay in ruins that Žižka had destroyed it.

Hrubá Skála

HRUBÁ SKÁLA

VOJMIL AND SVATAVA

In Bohemia there is a landscape that spreads out, delectable and pleasing, where the kneading fingers of the Creator stayed longer than elsewhere and where every corner betrays his joy in creation and his happy eye. It is called the Bohemian Paradise and there are in it many of those signs that make for paradise: the fragrant shade of woods and groves, the bright, lucid water of springs and the calm of woodland ponds, the smooth earth of the fields, the delicacy of flowering meadows, and rough cliffs too, sunny glades on the tops of hills and damp half-light in rocky ravines.

In the midst of this landscape there has stood since ancient times a firm castle on a rock that was like a nest of birds of prey. Its name was Hrubá Skála, which means a rough-hewn rock. Legend tells us that in the days of the Bohemian King Přemysl Ottakar I. the lord of this castle was Beneš Heřmanóv.

And those were again times when the muffled rattle of arms spilt across the mountains on the frontier of the country and a flood of armoured Saxons poured into Bohemia from the north. But while war threatened the country Beneš Heřmanóv was waging a different battle within his own family. His daughter Svatava had grown to the age of marriage, and her beauty and kind heart had captured the fancy of Vojmil, son of the lord of Zbiroh. But lord Beneš of Hrubá Skála had parted from the lord of Zbiroh in anger. So he had no love for his son. But he tried in vain to sever the invisible bonds that bound Svatava and Vojmil together. He did not know that no sword has ever been forged in the world that could overcome pure and enduring love.

The Saxons were already drawing their bow-strings in the Bohemian land and their lances and axes were coloured with blood. Pain and suffering had entered Bo-hemia, banners of black smoke fluttered on the horizon and people fled from the villages into the forest. Wrong was wedded to hatred, only Svatava and Vojmil thought of love and sent each other messages by a devoted servant, whom no one suspected of such errands.

The Saxons had already reached the crags of Trosky and were closing in on Hrubá Skála, they swarmed over the roads, searched the thickets and rocky holes, leading out hidden cattle and going back to their company with mooing booty.

Beneš Heřmanóv prepared for defence. He assembled his men and those of friendly knights in the cliffs below his castle and he waited. Report of the Saxon stealing and pillaging preceded the Saxon army and a mood of belligerence seized the Czechs. Spies ran up from the road to Prague and announced that the Saxons were on them. As when sparks hiss, as when a flock of eagles rus-tle their wings, so the forest opened and sparkled with a rippling and a rumbling and released militant Czechs from its shade. The two armies clashed. Lances were broken and blood-stained swords slashed the Saxons red cloaks. The cry of those who were wounding mixed with the cry of the wounded, frightened birds fled from the tree-tops, the cliffs trembled with the din of the battle and deer sought shelter in the deepest gorges.

There is an ominous cloud of Saxons and the Czech troops must fight doubly hard. Beneš Heřmanóv, sur-rounded by waves of Saxons, defends himself with his last ounce of strength. Indeed the strength of all the Czechs is failing and the Saxons feel that, despite their terrible losses, victory is veering to their side. Suddenly the forest opens for a second time, and from its green gates out rush horsemen clothed in black, fresh, with swords drawn. They hurl themselves on the Saxons and at once decide the battle. The knight who leads them carves his way through the enemy straight to Beneš of Hrubá Skála, who is in dire straits. He frees him from the grip of the enemy and leads him to a safe place. At that moment a Saxon rider gallops up on his horse and raises his sword against lord Beneš. But the unknown knight catches the blow and the Saxon's sword gashes his helmet. The Saxons retreat, the Saxons turn, the Saxons flee across fields and forests to the frontier of the Czech land. Beneš Heřmanóv looks round for his saviour. But where are the black-clothed fighters, and where is he who led them? The forest has fallen silent and has closed over the throng of saviours who decided the battle. It is locked with a songful key, for there was peace, the birds had come back and welcomed the silence and calm with song.

Svatava knew who it was who had come to help her father in his need. But she was afraid to betray the name of his saviour.

Then Beneš Heřmanóv had a great feast prepared at his castle for all his friends and allies and he declared that the knight who had held his head so that his helmet caught what would have been a fatal blow, should not go unrewarded. And if he was unmarried, he would give him his daughter as wife.

Lord Beneš fished so long for the truth till he fished out a lie. Some young man with a gashed helmet came forward and the castle lord received him with profuse thanks as his saviour. He sat him in the place of honour, served him himself with the choicest bits of meat and poured his wine. The young man made full use of the castle lord's favour, and he bid for the hand of Svatava, which belonged to him according to lord Beneš's promise.

"Behold", lord Beneš Heřmanóv addressed Svatava, "there is your bridegroom" and he pointed to the young man with the gashed helmet, "you will scarcely find a braver one. I shall arrange for your wedding celebrations this very week."

Svatava was frightened. She almost cried out that it was Vojmil who had saved her father and that the young man was lying. But then she said firmly:

"Rather than marry this man, I shall never marry at all."

Incensed, Beneš Heřmanóv sprang up suddenly from the table, till a pitcher overturned and wine dripped from the board like blood.

"It is my wish," he cried.

Svatava stood up in silence with tears in her eyes. Her father nodded and the guard came running. On the lord's command they took Svatava away to the castle's deepest dungeon. It was a dungeon hollowed out of the cliff, cold and damp, and both day and night dragged by in twilight there, for the window was so small, a mere crack in the cliff.

For seven days the father came to see his daughter there and demanded that she should obey him and marry the young man. And for seven days the daughter answered:

"I cannot marry him."

On the evening of the seventh day Beneš Heřmanóv decided he would have his daughter walled up. By the light of torches servants brought stones and walled up the dungeon with Svatava in it.

The water in Svatava's jug was running low. Weeping, she took leave of the world. She looked for the last time towards the narrow window and saw a single star in the night sky. She saw a single star and she heard a voice:

"Svatava, fear not, I am near you."

Confused, Svatava gazed at the star. Was it heaven speaking to her, or a human voice?

"It is I, Vojmil," she heard then, and the shadow of a human head appeared at the window.

Up the steep cliff Vojmil had climbed right to the castle dungeon. He tied himself with a rope and bit by bit broke off the sandstone rock around the window. Now he could give Svatava his hand, now he could hear the joyful beating of her heart. He presses her to him and lets himself down by the rope into the deep ravine.

As soon as his heels touch the moss and he lays the enfeebled Svatava on the grass the castle lord's men-at-arms run out of the young oak wood and Beneš Heřmanóv himself steps out before Svatava and Vojmil. "Hold up the light for me," he orders a man with a torch and surveys his daughter's abductor. He sees Vojmil clothed in black and he sees the wound on his forehead. He sees Svatava kneeling in the grass and his recognition and his sorrow prevent him from speaking.

They all return in silent procession to Hrubá Skála and the young swindler runs out past them and is lost in the forest.

And then Vojmil and Svatava had a glorious wedding, and there were so many lights in the castle that it glowed as if it was burning. And all those lights still shine today to light the way for those who love each other so much that neither wall nor cliff can bury their love.

Trosky

TROSKY

TWO VOICES

From Trosky, which means "ruins" and which are the ruins of an ancient castle, there opens out one of the most beautiful views in Bohemia, a view over the region that is known as the Czech Paradise.

In the 15th century two women lived in the mighty castle of Trosky, but they took no notice at all of the resplendent view spread before them.

They could see nothing but their immense hatred of one another.

They were Barbora of Bergov, the young widow of the lord of the castle, and Margaret of Bergov, that young lady's grandmother.

The first was a Protestant, the second a Catholic. Yet neither the one nor the other had taken to heart the Christian teaching of conciliation and humility...

As the first ray of the dawn sun fell on Trosky one of them started screaming at the other and they quarrelled till darkness fell...

So as to live as far from each other as they could, they each moved to one of the castle towers, the young woman to the slender one, the old woman to the bulky one.

But the distance between the two towers was not so great that their hatred could not overcome it.

The shouts from one tower flew to the other only to come back still louder, still more ominous...

For years the grandmother and grand-daughter screamed at each other, they were both quite hoarse, but for all those years they never found a better way of spending their lives.

Then the old woman died.

The young one was lonely.

All day long she gazed at the other tower, as if waiting impatiently to hear a voice from there...

In the translucent morning light there was no sound but silence.

And the far horizons stretched away into endless distance.

It is told that the young woman began to cry...

Was she remembering the old woman?

Had she understood the vanity of hatred? The uselessness of screaming?

Did she regret those lost years? Had she understood Holy Writ?

When you climb up to Trosky you can look in the direction of someone whom you do not love.

And you can listen to the translucent silence...

ZBRASLAV

A LATE DECISION

The place on which Zbraslav castle stands today has a great tradition. A double tradition. It was a favourite seat of the Bohemian kings. King Přemysl Ottakar II. built a hunting lodge on the site of the old market, one of the oldest in Bohemia. And during his reign the castle was full of pleasures and delight.

But a basic change came about under King Wenceslas II. While he was on the throne the mood in Zbraslav was entirely different. The young king wanted to redress the guilt he felt over the execution of Záviš of Falkenštejn (related in this book in the story about Hluboká castle). He founded a magnificent monastery for Cistercian monks and chose Zbraslav as the place where members of the royal family were to be buried. He founded Zbraslav church for this very purpose.

And King Wenceslas II. himself spent some time in a monk's cell in Zbraslav, where he meditated on the sense of life, on the transience that concerns kings in the same way as beggars, he meditated on the places where his ancestor "the king of iron and gold", Přemysl Ottakar II. had shone. The surroundings of Zbraslav monastery had inclined people to contemplation for centuries.

One day another Bohemian king entered its walls. A seventeen-year-old king. Wenceslas III.

Shyly he walked through the dusk of the nave, he had come to pray at the grave of his father, who had lain for a year in his monastery grave.

The young king was the last of his line. The last of one of the oldest ruling families of Europe. For half a thousand years his family had ruled the Czech Lands, but today the House of the Přemyslides had, as it was said, only two eyes. The eyes of the seventeen-year-old king.

When he had become king he was sixteen.

He at once fell into the snares, spending days and nights at feasts, engaged in noisy amusements, in the company of idlers...

Now he stood in the church and watched the mystical flickering of the candles.

A great silence washed over the king's heart.

And the king was approached by the old abbot, friend of the king who lay in the grave before them.

He addressed the young man. And they spoke together at length, only when the sun rose over Zbraslav did the youthful king and the wise old man cease their conversation.

And the young king understood...

He felt a new tide of strength—he would be the most famous king of the royal house, rejecting weakness, did not the old prophesy say that the House of the Přemyslides was to rule to all eternity...?

And it is said that in Zbraslav a light shone on Wenceslas III. that lit up his life and showed him how vainly he had lived...

And the king changed. He cast off his old friends, those riotous livers who had been his favourites.

He summoned the Bohemian parliament. And decided to bring his kingdom to new glory.

Too late... He had not the time.

The time we each have for our deeds is strictly measured.

And our longings are longer than our time.

On 21st June 1306 the young king stood in Zbraslav church and decided on how he would live, on 4th August 1306 he was murdered in Olomouc by an unknown man.

The "eternal" dynasty of the Přemyslides was ended. The last of the Přemyslide eyes were closed.

In Zbraslav today we walk in the footsteps of so many Bohemian kings, including those of Wenceslas III. We too can meditate, perhaps a light will shine on us too that will clearly light up the form of our lives. There is still time... Still?

BLANÍK

THE KNIGHTS OF BLANÍK

There are hills from which you can look out to the distant country, and there are hills from which you can see far beyond the horizon into the depths of the past, from where legends grow. There have been hard times in Bohemia. As wasps fly down on a sweet tart, so from ancient days have enemies thrown themselves on the riches of our country. Throngs of them flowed in many streams over the land, they besieged castles, killed and plundered in the villages. The smoke of fires darkened the sky and the way of the enemy was the way of destruction.

It is said that once an enemy army penetrated to the place where the mighty hill Blaník towers to the sky. The enemy passed through a country without people. Everyone had fled to Blaník at the news of the approaching army. At the top of Blaník there were fortifications, ramparts and earthworks. Here, to this fortified place, people had brought all that was of most value to them, they had brought grain and even driven their cattle behind the walls.

And the enemy closed in like storm clouds and surrounded the hill with the fortified crown. There stood the Czechs, led by Zdeněk Zásmucký, and opposing them down below an enemy greatly superior in numbers.

Indeed numbers were on the side of the foreigners, but on the side of the Czechs was bravery.

Seven times the foreign bands charged in attack against the Czech ramparts, seven times they rushed up the steep slopes, forging their way through bushes, slipping on boulders, and seven times they were rebuffed. Ravens circled over the side of the hill, scenting prey.

Those in the Czech camp who carried arms fell asleep on the ramparts, exhausted, and there was no one to

Pecka

relieve them. Many Czechs were wounded and many Czechs died.

The enemy commander chose fresh warriors from his mighty army and attacked again. Day and night became a single battle. The grass below the fortifications was red with the blood of the enemy.Dawn broke in battle and in battle the day drew to its close. Amongst the Czechs behind the fortifications there were more dead than living.

And when the enemy attacked the Czech ramparts for the last time, his cries were answered by silence. The foreign troops climbed the earthworks and stood amidst a dead fort. The Czech warriors lay lifeless on the ground that they had defended to their last breath and grasped motionless weapons in their dead fingers.

The enemy army took the supplies and amassed treasures from the fort on the top of Blaník and marched on. Blaník was deserted.

Night followed day and day followed night. The moon in the heavens waxed and waned and waxed again. The wounds that the enemy had inflicted on the land began to heal, and people returned to the country below Blaník. Friends of those who had fallen on Blaník.

They climbed up the slope to the ramparts and looked for their dear ones in the fort, but there was just grass growing everywhere and no sign of any people. There was no one they could honour with burial. Nor did they even see the bones of dead horses. They could find no explanation.

When a year had passed a peasant on the slopes of Blaník heard a great hubbub inside the hill. Horses were beating their hoofs on the rocks there and neighing and weapons jangled. The peasant ran to the village and brought other people to listen to what was going on in the hill. They listened and their hearts were gripped by anxiety. The noise and tumult in Blaník reminded them of the noise of an army preparing to attack.

And in the time that followed many strange and unseen things occurred. Once a villager met Zdeněk Zásmucký and his companions by the river Blanice. All of them were on horseback. The villager hid himself in the bushes and saw the knights watering their horses in the river. Another time a ploughman saw a knightly retinue riding towards Blaník. He left his plough and followed the retinue out of curiosity. The knights came to the hillside, which opened up before them and then quietly closed behind them.

But the strangest event was experienced by a shepherd who was grazing his sheep below Blaník. In the evening, when he wanted to drive the flock home, he noticed that a wether was missing. He left the flock with his dog and went to look for the wether. It was dusk in the forest, night was preparing to settle down in the thickets, and before the shepherd was a cliff with an opening in the middle that seemed to invite him. The shepherd hesitated at the dark opening, but then he said to himself: maybe the wether wandered in. He bent his head and stepped into the darkness. Hardly was he inside than he heard a slight creaking sound. He looked round—and the cliff had closed behind him. He was standing in a stone passage. At the end of the passage a faint light glimmered. The shepherd made for the light and came into a vast hall with a high ceiling.As far as he could see, everywhere warriors were lying and sleeping. They did not sleep as men sleep in peacetime. They slept like men at war, clothed, belted, with helmets on their heads, swords ready to hand, they slept sitting, as if between two battles, ready to leap up at the first call. The amazed shepherd walked amongst them and saw sleeping horses, saddled and prepared to set out at any moment. And as the shepherd went he felt drowsiness overcoming him. He sat down in the nearest corner, leant his back against the cliff and fell asleep like the knights.

He was awoken by a clamour, the clashing of weapons and shields. All round him the knights were getting up, mounting their horses, and just opposite the shepherd the cliff opened up as if a castle gateway was being opened. Through the gateway he could see the forest and the meadow where he had grazed his sheep in the evening.

The shepherd got up off the ground and wanted to run to his flock. But one of the men-at-arms stepped in his way and laid a hand on his shoulder.

"Do not forget," he addressed the shepherd, "that all of us, as you see us here, are ready to plunge into the fight again. Tell all the living that we are standing guard for ever. When the worst befalls our country, it will find help and protection with us. And convey to those above too that they should defend their country and its rights to the last breath, as we defended it."

The shepherd never quite knew how he got out of the rocky hall. He did not find his flock in the meadow. He hurried home, confused and frightened. In the village they welcomed him as if he had risen from the dead. A year had passed between his going and his coming back. He had slept through a whole year in Blaník.

The shepherd told what had happened to him and the story of the Knights of Blaník crossed mountains and rivers. It was said that every year, on the day that Blaník was conquered by the enemy, the earth opens up and warriors in full armour ride out of Blaník on their horses. They practise shooting and wrestling after their year's sleep. Lastly they water their horses in the Blanice and ride back into Blaník.

There have been hard times in Bohemia. But the worst has never yet befallen, so that the Knights of Blaník had to ride out of the hill and come to the aid of their country. And even when it seemed that all was lost, the living were able to defend their rights with wisdom and weapons. And it is said that those who fell in the just struggle went down to the Knights of Blaník in the rocky hall and there the heroes are standing guard for ever.

Eduard Petiška (1924–1987) is one of the best-known Czech writers. He is the author of numerous works both for the adult and young reader. Many of his seventy books met with a wide international acceptance. They have been translated into 27 languages and published in hundreds of editions abroad. The number of copies of Petiška's books has exceeded 10 million. "A Treasury of Tales from the Kingdom of Bohemia" ranks among the author's books devoted to myths and legends. In this group there appeared the legends of ancient Israel, Greece, Egypt and Mesopotamia, the stories of "A Thousand And One Nights" and a two volume book of legends from Bohemia, Moravia and Silesia.

EDUARD PETIŠKA:
A TREASURY OF TALES FROM THE KINGDOM OF BOHEMIA

Would you like to learn of the ancient history
of the famous Bohemian kingdom?
To enter the enchanting world of ancient legends?
To read of great Bohemian kings, saints, knights
and the ordinary people of the Czech Lands?

A Treasury of Tales from the Kingdom of Bohemia is the name
of the book that invites you on a journey into the world of Czech
legends. Here a great story-teller brings you exciting stories of
bygone centuries, describes events in the ancient mighty kingdom
of Bohemia. The captivating stories contained in this book have
originated over long centuries, since mythical times. Rare draw-
ings, not published in centuries, add to the charm
of this remarkable book.

The stories may also be used
as an excellent tourist guide for visitors to Bohemia.

Orders for the Czech, English and German versions
can be sent to the distributors
Baset
U Sanopzu 5
15000 Prague 5
The Czech Republic

EDUARD PETIŠKA

A TREASURY OF TALES

FROM

THE KINGDOM OF BOHEMIA

MARTIN

Orders may be sent to the same address for stories
by Eduard Petiška on the lives of the three great saints
from the dawn of Czech national history

THE LIVES OF ST. WENCESLAS, ST. LUDMILA AND ST. ADALBERT

*Would you like to know more about the life of Wenceslas,
prince and saint?*
Or the fate of St. Ludmila, who was his grandmother?
Do you know the facts of the turbulent life of St. Adalbert?

This book presents three Bohemian saints from the dawn
of Czech national history and brings their time attractively
near. The description of the beginnings of Christianity
in Bohemia is accompanied by old drawings that have not
been published in centuries, and delightfully catch the
mood of the stories.

The Baset network distributes this book
in English and German.

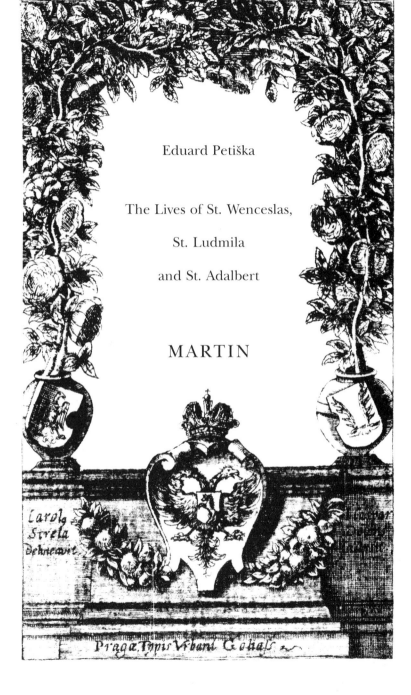

Eduard Petiška

The Lives of St. Wenceslas,

St. Ludmila

and St. Adalbert

MARTIN

CONTENTS

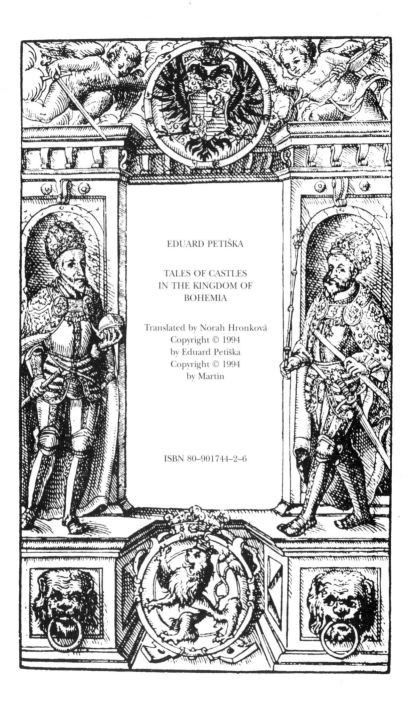

EDUARD PETIŠKA

TALES OF CASTLES
IN THE KINGDOM OF
BOHEMIA

Translated by Norah Hronková
Copyright © 1994
by Eduard Petiška
Copyright © 1994
by Martin

ISBN 80–901744–2–6